MAMMOTHS MASTODONS AND MAN

ILLUSTRATIONS BY DALE GRABEL

McGRAW-HILL BOOK COMPANY

New York · Toronto · London · Sydney
St. Louis · San Francisco · Mexico · Panama

BY ROBERT SILVERBERG

MAMMOTHS MASTODONS AND MAN

11776

CONTENTS

CHAPTER ONE 9   GIANTS IN THE EARTH

CHAPTER TWO 25   THE SIBERIAN MAMMOTHS

CHAPTER THREE 55   BEHEMOTH IN THE NEW WORLD

CHAPTER FOUR 83   "MAMMOTH FEVER"

CHAPTER FIVE 96   MAMMOTHS, MEN, AND ICE

CHAPTER SIX 130   MASTODONS WITH HORNS AND OTHER WONDERS

CHAPTER SEVEN 153   THE FAMILY TREE OF THE ELEPHANTS

CHAPTER EIGHT 191   AMERICA'S ANCIENT MASTODON HUNTERS

MAMMOTHS MASTODONS AND MAN

CHAPTER ONE

GIANTS IN THE EARTH

The sixth chapter of Genesis, which describes the world at the time when Noah was told to build his Ark, says, "There were giants in the earth in those days." But when Noah invited the beasts and the birds aboard the Ark, the giants were not included; and when the great Deluge came, they must have perished along with all other living things that Noah left behind.

And the waters of the flood drew back, and the earth reappeared, and it was peopled again by the children of Noah, and by the offspring of the creatures that had been taken into the Ark.

And, thousands of years later, men began to dig up the bones of the vanished giants.

About 1400, according to an English chronicler,

there were found at the seashore in Essex "two teeth of a certain giant of such a huge bigness that two hundred such teeth as men have nowadays might be cut out of them."

The discovery of a giant's thighbone in Vienna in 1443 caused tremendous excitement throughout Austria. It was found by workmen digging the foundation for a new tower for St. Stephen's Cathedral. A mason chiseled the year and the Austrian national motto into the colossal bone, and it was chained for a while to one of the cathedral's doors, which afterwards was nicknamed The Giant's Door.

In 1577 a storm toppled a large oak tree growing near Lucerne, Switzerland. Some men peering under the fallen tree's roots caught sight of what they imagined were human bones. They brought them to the town authorities, who decided to rebury them in Lucerne's cemetery. First, though, the bones were examined by a learned physician, Dr. Felix Platter. He pointed out that this was no ordinary skeleton; it was the remains of a giant nineteen or twenty feet tall. Since such a giant could only have lived before Noah's Deluge, he obviously had not been a Christian, and therefore was not eligible for burial in the local graveyard. Instead the huge bones went on exhibition in the town hall of Lucerne as curiosities, and they remained on display for more than two hundred years.

Giants' bones began to turn up in France in 1456, when a vast skull, some immense teeth, and other such things were found by the side of a river near Valence. The skull was measured at a width of two cubits—about three feet—and a shoulderblade was six cubits across. One expert on giants inspected the relics and concluded that this particular giant must have been fifteen cubits—or twenty-three feet—in height.

The neighborhood around Valence was rich in such extraordinary items. The remains of an eighteen-foot-high giant found there were placed on display at a church in Bourges by order of King Louis XI. The teeth of another giant, weighing ten pounds each, were hung in a different church. In 1564, peasants saw giant bones sticking out of the ground near the banks of the Rhone. Obviously this part of France—the province known as the Dauphiné—had had an unusually large population of giants in the days before God sent the Deluge to destroy the wicked world. One district of the province contained so many giant bones that it became known as *Le Champs des Géants*, "the field of giants."

The most widely discussed discovery ever made in the field of giants came on January 11, 1613, near the castle of Chaumont. A nearly complete skeleton of some gigantic creature was found. Somehow a local surgeon named Mazurier took charge of the excavation and issued some startling details. The skeleton, he said, was 25½ feet long, 10 feet wide across the shoulders, and 5 feet deep from the breast to the back. Each tooth was as big as an ox's foot, and the shinbone alone was four feet in length. According to Mazurier, this marvel was contained in a brick tomb 30 feet long, 12 feet wide, and 8 feet high, buried 16 feet below the surface of the ground. Inscribed on the tomb, he claimed, was the inscription, *Teutobo-chus Rex.*

Teutobochus had been one of the barbarian chieftains who had made war on Rome; he was king of the Germanic tribe known as the Cimbri, and supposedly was a man of great height. In 102 B.C. he had been defeated by the Roman general Marius in a battle 18 miles north of Marseilles.

French scholars were not greatly impressed by Mazurier's claim to have found the grave of King Teutobochus. Nobody but Mazurier himself, it seems, ever got to see the brick tomb or its alleged inscription. However, the bones were undeniably genuine and undeniably gigantic. Whose bones were they, though?

Many learned Frenchmen were willing to believe that even if the bones were not really those of Teutobochus, they must surely have come from some other human giant—most likely one of the giants that the Bible said had lived before the Deluge. But a few skeptical scientists pointed out that the skeleton from the field of giants did not look much like that of a man. The "arms" hardly seemed like arms at all; they were more like the front legs of some four-legged beast. The head was too big for the body. No, it was hardly a human skeleton at all. Rather, it seemed to be the skeleton of a large animal, something about the size and general shape of an elephant.

One man of the early seventeenth century actually said the bones *were* those of an elephant. He was the physician Jean Riolan, an expert on anatomy, who wrote a book supporting his idea. But to most people it was absurd to think that tropical beasts such as elephants had ever lived in France.

Aside from the "giant" theory, there was a much more curious explanation for the presence of huge bones in the earth. This was that what had been found was not a skeleton at all, but a freak of nature —a type of mineral that just accidentally happened to have taken the shape of giant bones.

This idea went back to early medieval times, and had often been used to account for some of the strange things that had been dug up in Europe. Not all of the bones that were uncovered could easily be considered to be those of giants; some of them had weird horns or tusks or fangs, and plainly belonged to animals that no living man had ever beheld. These vast and unknown creatures might have been dragons or griffins, perhaps. But why were they never seen alive? Could it be that they were the relics of animals that no longer existed on the earth?

That went against the accepted religious teachings. The Bible said that God had ordered Noah to bring into the Ark "every living thing of all flesh." He might have left the giants behind, since they were only human beings of great size. But would Noah have allowed entire groups of animals to meet death when the waters rose?

Since that seemed impossible, other explanations were needed for these objects, which were called fossils (from the Latin word *fossilis,* meaning "dug up"). In the eleventh century one philosopher suggested that they were products of the *vis plastica,*

the "molding force," which prankishly compelled
rock to take on the appearance of the bones of bizarre creatures. In the thirteenth century the idea
was put forward that the fossils were "models of
God's rejected works" or "outlines of future crea-
tions."

The trouble with this kind of ingenuity, though, is
that it did not stand up to much investigation. Anyone who broke open one of the fossils could see that
its internal structure looked exactly like the internal
structure of a real bone. Was it likely that the *vis
plastica* would have filled the earth with rocks that
looked so much like bones, inside and out? It seemed
much more probable to reasonable people that the
fossils really were bones. And so the notion of a *vis
plastica* faded away.

Most people, if they thought about the fossils at
all, stuck to the simplest available explanation: that
the big bones were the remains of giants drowned in
the Deluge. The bones of the weird dragons and
other monsters continued to provide a problem,
though. Those brave men who dared to defy the
Church still argued that they were the relics of
beasts that perished in the Deluge and no longer existed in the world. They were *antediluvian,* or pre-
Deluge, animals.

By the middle of the seventeenth century, religious leaders began to yield on that point. Since no
other way of accounting for the most peculiar fossils could be found, the churches started to agree
that they were indeed the bones of antediluvian animals that God had decided to wipe from existence. It

seemed odd that He would go to the bother of creating such beasts only to destroy them; but who were mere men to try to understand God's deeds?

And still the bones of giants came from the earth. In 1644, during a period of war between Austria and Sweden, the citizens of the Austrian town of Krems were enlarging their town's fortifications when they uncovered a tooth weighing almost two pounds. A year later, the Swedes conquered Krems and began to build fortifications of their own, including a stronghold on a hill near the place where the giant's tooth was found. In the process of digging a ditch to carry rain water away from the construction site, the workmen made a new discovery, which was described in these words in *Theatrum Europaeum* ("The Theater of Europe"), a book issued in 1647 by the Swiss artist and publisher Matthäus Merian:

"It then happened that they, in that ditch about three or four cubits under the surface found . . . a gigantic large body of a giant, of which (while the work progressed and before it had been recognized as a body) the head and some limbs had been destroyed because everything was soft and rotten with age. But still many parts remained that were looked at by learned and experienced men and were declared human limbs. . . ." The head, said Merian, must have been "as large as a round table." The arms were "as thick as the body of a man," and "one tooth alone weighs five and one half pounds."

The bones of several "giants" discovered in Germany in 1663 included a feature apparently not common in previous finds: enormous tusks. Workers quarrying gypsum near the town of Quedlingburg found them in a large mass of mixed-up bones. Otto von Guericke, the mayor of the city of Magdeburg, examined the bones and came to the conclusion that they could not be those of a human being, since no man before or after the Deluge, giant or normal in size, had ever had such immense horns—as he thought the tusks to be. He decided that the skeletons were those of unicorns, and he produced a sketch of a fantastic giant creature with a single massive horn in the middle of its forehead and a dozen teeth a foot long in each jaw. Some years later the German scientist and philosopher Gottfried Wilhelm Leibnitz printed Guericke's unicorn sketch in one of his books, and made it famous throughout Europe.

Guericke had taken an important step forward in the understanding of ancient life by trying to reconstruct the Quedlingburg bones. Unfortunately, he put them together in a way that we now know was altogether wrong; but his attempt was more useful than saying that the bones were the remains of antediluvian giant men.

Relics of giants were turning up in the New World too, now. In 1705, an enormous tooth and bones were found at Claverack, New York, a town near the Hudson River. The tooth weighed nearly five pounds; one thighbone was said to be seventeen feet in length. Joseph Dudley, the governor of Massachusetts, learned of these wonders and sent word of them to Cotton Mather, the famous Puritan philosopher and scholar. "I am perfectly of the opinion," Dudley wrote, "that the tooth will agree only to the human body, for whom the Flood only could prepare a funeral. . . ." Wishing to examine the bones, Mather learned that they had crumbled to pieces soon after they had been exposed to the air, but he was able to see and measure another giant's tooth that had been discovered in the same neighborhood. In 1712 he sent an account of the various giant fossils to his friend Dr. John Woodward of London, and two years later a summary of Mather's letter to Woodward was published in the *Philosophical Transactions* of the Royal Society of London. This report quotes Mather as saying that the great tooth is similar to a human eyetooth: "It has four Prongs, or Roots, flat, and something worn on the top; it was six inches high, lacking one eighth, as it stood upright on its Roots and almost thirteen inches in circumference; it weigh'd two pounds four ounces Troy weight."

These remarks attracted much attention. But this was not the first published report of American giants. In 1632, an account of the conquest of Mexico by Cortés had been printed in Spain; it had been written some sixty years earlier by Bernal Díaz de Castillo, who as a young man had been part of Cortés' small army. Bernal Díaz' narrative relates how in 1519 the Spaniards came to the Mexican city-state of Tlaxcala, whose people told them "that in ancient times the land was inhabited by men and women of immense stature and wicked ways." The Tlaxcalans claimed that their ancestors had eventu-

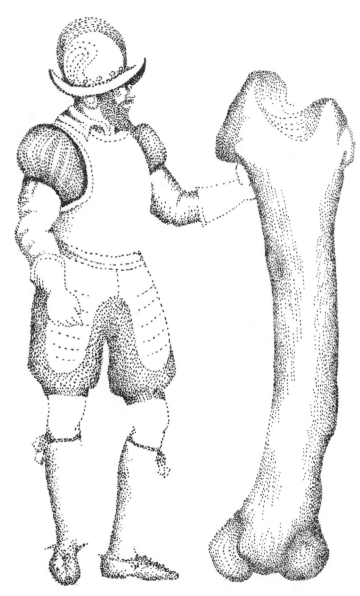

Cortez looking at thighbone
of a ''giant'' (a mammoth bone)

ally wiped these evil giants out. "And in order that we might judge of their size," Bernal Díaz says, "they brought us a thighbone of a man of this race. It was so large that when placed upright it was as high as a man of average size. I stood beside it, and found that it was as tall as myself, though I am as tall as most men. They brought also other pieces of other bones of great size, but much decayed by time; but the one I have mentioned was entire; we were astonished at these remains, and thought that they certainly proved the former existence of giants." Cortés ordered that the Tlaxcala bone be sent to Spain for the amusement of Emperor Charles V. It was the first fossil ever sent to Europe from the New World, but we are not told if the Emperor, who was more interested in gold than in bones, was pleased with it.

But by the time Cotton Mather wrote his account of the teeth and bones found in 1705, the idea that these were the remains of giant men was beginning to lose support. It now seemed more and more probable that Jean Riolan had been right, and that the fossils were those of elephants.

It was hard to believe that elephants had ever roamed the forests of Europe, but the evidence was steadily mounting. About 1630 a huge skeleton was dug up at Tunis, in North Africa, and, as was usual at that time, it was identified as that of a giant. A French traveler who was present sent one of its teeth to his friend, the scholar Nicolas Peiresc. Some time later, a live elephant was exhibited in France, such a beast then being an extremely rare sight in Europe. Peiresc went to see the animal, and arranged to borrow it long enough to make a wax cast of its teeth. In this way he discovered that the fossil tooth sent to him from Tunis was remarkably similar to the tooth of a modern elephant.

Then, later in the seventeenth century, workmen digging a canal in Belgium unearthed two nearly complete skeletons of tusk-bearing animals that were obviously elephants. This was the first time that fossils of this sort had been found in good enough condition to make it clear what kind of animals they had been.

In 1687, large bones came to light in Italy. Again, the peasants called them "giants' bones," but a local doctor took the trouble to compare them with the skeleton of a modern elephant that belonged to a museum in Florence. The two skeletons were very much alike.

By the beginning of the eighteenth century, a good many European men of science were no longer able to deny that the so-called "giants' bones" that had been found so often were actually the bones of elephants. But how had there happened to be so many elephants in Europe in the past, if none lived there now?

Some people said that the bones must be those of circus elephants that had died and been buried. Thus when a number of elephant bones were found in a field near London, the story spread that they were those of an elephant that had belonged to a traveling show called Wombwell's Menagerie. When workmen digging in Oxford also came upon elephants' bones,

they insisted that those, too, must have been the remains of a Wombwell's Menagerie beast.

But the proprietors of the Wombwell show denied
having buried any elephants anywhere. And it was
plainly ridiculous to credit the "giants' bones" to
such an origin, since only a handful of elephants—so
to speak—had ever been brought to Europe as sideshow exhibits. At any one time there were rarely
more than one or two elephants to be seen in all of
Europe; people made long journeys to have a
chance to view these fabulous and exotic creatures.
Yet the bones of many dozens of elephants had been
unearthed during the past few centuries.

Historians ransacked their archives for instances
of the shipment of elephants to Europe. They
discovered that on a number of occasions European
monarchs had brought elephants back from abroad
as souvenirs of their travels, or had been sent elephants as gifts from admiring Oriental rulers.
When King Louis IX of France came home from
Palestine in 1254, after having spent six years
fighting in the Crusades, he brought an elephant
with him that he had acquired in North Africa. Another Crusader, the Holy Roman Emperor Frederick
II, also came home with an elephant when he returned to Italy from the Holy Land in 1231. Four
hundred years earlier, Caliph Harun al-Rashid of
Baghdad had shipped an elephant to France as a
token of his friendship for the Emperor Charle-
magne. And there were other such stories.

For wholesale importation of elephants into Europe, though, it was necessary to look farther back

in time. In the third century B.C., hundreds of elephants had been used as instruments of war in the long, bitter conflict between Rome and her great rival, the North African city of Carthage. The first time Carthage used elephants against Rome was in 218 B.C. In that year the great Carthaginian general Hannibal took thirty-seven terrifying, trained war elephants with his army when he set out on an invasion of Europe. Hannibal sailed to Spain, across the Mediterranean from Carthage, and marched eastward through what is now France and then was called Gaul. He crossed the Alps with his elephants and struck deep into Italy. In battle, the elephants charged like living tanks, smashing through the Roman infantry lines and sending soldiers scattering in panic.

Most of Hannibal's elephants, unaccustomed to the chilly European weather, died in the mountain passes before the Carthaginian army reached Italy. Nevertheless, Hannibal conquered much of the territory surrounding Rome, and came close to conquering Rome itself. But in later battles the Romans learned how to cope with Hannibal's elephants—by stepping aside and letting the big beasts run harmlessly through the openings in their battle line—and eventually Carthage was defeated.

The Romans themselves used war elephants of their own when they invaded Britain in A.D. 43 in the reign of the Emperor Claudius. The Britons put up a fierce, stubborn resistance, but the presence of these strange and gigantic animals on the Roman side did much to bring about their defeat.

Eighteenth-century scientists and historians, therefore, fell back on the elephants of Hannibal and Claudius to account for all the discoveries of "giants' bones." Bones found between Spain and Italy were obviously those of Hannibal's elephants; those found in Britain must have come over with the Romans. Thus when a pharmacist named Conyers dug up some elephant bones in London in 1715, he wrote, "How this elephant came there is the question. I know some will have it to have lain there ever since the Universal Deluge. For my own part, I take it to have been brought over with many others by the Romans in the reign of Claudius the Emperor. . . ." A stone ax made from a piece of chipped flint was lying with the bones. Conyers decided that this was the weapon with which some valiant Briton had slain the great beast in a battle.

By the middle of the eighteenth century, enormous numbers of fossil elephants had been credited to the armies of Hannibal and Claudius. But objections were raised. For one thing, a single section of Italy had yielded the bones of more elephants than Carthage had ever sent into battle in all its wars.

For another, many of the elephants that were unearthed were found complete with their tusks. Assuming that the Romans and the Carthaginians would have gone to the trouble of burying dead elephants in the first place, why would these people—who prized ivory greatly—have buried their valuable tusks? And some of the elephants were buried twenty feet or more down in the ground, or in awkward hillside positions.

What made the war-elephant theory seem even less probable was the discovery of fossil bones in Europe belonging to such other tropical beasts as the hippopotamus, the rhinoceros, and the hyena. Nowhere did history declare that the Romans or anybody else had brought large numbers of hippopotamuses into Europe. The only possible conclusion was that at some time in the past Europe must have had a climate in which the warmth-loving beasts of Africa—including the elephant—had been able to live.

The final blow to the accepted explanations of the elephant bones came from the north, in the reports of travelers who had been to the frozen wastelands of Siberia. Elephant fossils were found there too! If elephants could have lived at the edge of the Arctic, they could certainly have lived in England. The discovery of these huge bones forced men to take a new look at their theories about the past—and led to some surprising and disturbing conclusions.

THE SIBERIAN MAMMOTHS

CHAPTER TWO

Siberia is a vast and largely forlorn region of the Soviet Union stretching from the Ural Mountains in the west to the Pacific Ocean in the east, and from the Arctic Ocean in the north to the borders of China and Mongolia in the south. It is half again as large as the continental United States (excluding Alaska), but it has fewer people than New York State and New England combined. Siberian winters are legendary for their fierceness; —50° is an ordinary sort of temperature there in January, and temperatures close to —100° afflict some of the more remote settlements of the north.

Great stretches of Siberia are covered by thick forests through which mighty rivers flow. But in the north there is a dreary and inhospitable wasteland, the *tundra,* where trees and shrubs cannot grow and ice and snow cover everything for nine or ten months a year. The tundra, and much of the rest of Siberia, is a land gripped by *permafrost,* perpetually frozen ground, cold and rock-hard to depths of up to a thousand feet. In Siberia's brief summer, the uppermost few feet of permafrost may thaw, turning the ground to thick mud, but below the mud line the earth remains locked in the deepest of deep freezes.

This terrible land of frost and bitter cold is, however, a storehouse of natural wealth. Oil, metals, timber, and coal abound in Siberia; the rivers teem with fish; valuable fur-bearing animals such as ermine, white fox, muskrat, and sable live in its forests. Nomadic huntsmen long have wandered Siberia's grim terrain, searching for these beasts, whose skins and furs command such high prices in more comfortable parts of the world. They trap their prey in the snow-choked forests and even follow the hardiest animals far to the north, into the forbidding tundra country.

Of all the commodities that found their way from Siberia to the outer world, though, the most precious probably was ivory, until quite recent times. Ivory comes from the tusks of elephants; and elephants, being warmth-loving beasts, do not inhabit Siberia. Yet Siberia was for many centuries one of the chief sources of supply for ivory.

Chinese merchants began buying Siberian ivory more than two thousand years ago. The Chinese did not think that the ivory came from elephants, however; they knew that the Siberians dug it out of the earth, and believed that it came from a kind of gigantic mole or rat that lived underground, tunneling through the ice with two huge teeth. The seventeenth-century Chinese Emperor K'ang-hsi wrote a book on animals in which he mentioned reading in certain ancient works ''about the *fen-shü,* the underground rat of the north, which is also called 'the rat beneath the ice.' There is in the north in the country of the Olosses near the sea, a kind of rat as big as an elephant which lives underground and dies as soon as it comes into the air or is reached by the sunlight.'' The emperor added, ''There are *fen-shü* which weigh as much as 10,000 pounds. Their teeth [tusks] are like those of elephants; the natives of the north make bowls, combs, and knife-handles, etc. out of them. I have myself seen these teeth and these tools made from them and so I believe in the truth of our ancient books.''

Another Chinese book on natural history, written in the sixteenth century, quotes a work dating from the fourth century B.C. concerning a beast called *yen-shü,* ''the self-concealing mouse,'' native to northern countries: ''It is found in holes in the ground, has the appearance of a mouse, but is as large as a buffalo. It has no tail and is of a dark color. Its strength is very great, and it digs itself into holes in the ground in hilly and woody places.'' The sixteenth-century book adds that a different writer says that this animal ''frequents only dark and solitary places, and dies when it sees the rays of the sun or moon.''

Pliny the Elder, the great Roman scholar of the first century A.D., learned at third or fourth hand that there was a place far away where ivory was dug out of the ground. He had not heard the Chinese legend of giant underground rats with tusks, or he would surely have printed it in his *Natural History,* a collection of scientific information that included all sorts of fantastic fables accepted as truth. Instead he believed that the underground ivory came from elephants, and in his chapter on those animals he wrote, "When their tusks have fallen off, either by accident or from old age, they bury them in the earth."

Early in the tenth century A.D. the Arabs became involved in the Siberian ivory trade. Arab traders found their way to Bolgari, a town on the Volga River in what is now Russia; here, near the western border of Siberia, they saw in the marketplace certain bones, tusks, and teeth of extraordinary size. The teeth were quite similar to those of an elephant, but no one in Bolgari knew what animal they had come from, only that the source of the relics was deep in the northeast, across the mountains in Siberia. The Arab traders bought the tusks, took them home, and cut them up into combs, vases, and other ornamental objects that were sold for a good profit. For several centuries thereafter, Arab merchants journeyed to Bolgari and neighboring towns along the Volga in order to buy the ivory from Siberia.

English voyagers began to enter Russia in the middle of the sixteenth century. Soon there was thriving trade between England and Russia, and some of the bolder Englishmen ventured into the most distant and forbidding regions of the north. Among them was Josias Logan, who in July, 1611, explored Russia's coastline on the Arctic Sea, just west of the Ural mountain chain that divides Russia from Siberia. This region was inhabited by the Samoyeds, a tribe of semi-nomadic people who kept herds of reindeer and hunted the animals of the tundra. One of these Samoyeds sold Logan a piece of an elephant's tusk. Logan shipped it to England, and in a letter to the geographer Richard Hakluyt he expressed his surprise at finding such a strange object in the frozen north. The commodities in which the Samoyeds deal, Logan wrote, "may be such as we dreamed not on yet."

Logan's tusk gave Europe its first indication that there was ivory in Siberia. The English traders in Russia purchased a good deal of this ivory in the seventeenth century, but no one attempted to explain how elephants happened to be living in so cold a place. When an explanation finally was put forward, it was the wrong one. A French Jesuit priest, Father Avril, who visited Siberia about 1685, declared that the Siberian ivory came from animals found in the waters of the Arctic Ocean and the rivers flowing into it. He wrote:

"The Russians have discovered a sort of ivory which is whiter and smoother than that which comes from India. Not that they have any elephants that furnish them with this commodity, but other amphibious animals which they call by the name of Behemot, which are usually found in the River Lena,

Siberian merchant of mammoth ivory

or on the shores of the Tartarian Sea [the Arctic Ocean]. . . . Nor are elephants' teeth comparable to them, either for beauty or whiteness; besides that, they have a peculiar property to staunch blood, being carried about a person subject to bleeding. The Persians and Turks, who buy them up, put a high value upon them, and prefer a scimitar or a dagger haft of this precious ivory before a handle of massy gold or silver."

The creature that produces the ivory, Father Avril asserted, "is as big and dangerous as a crocodile." He told how the natives of the region "go frequently upon the side of the frozen sea to hunt this monster, and because it requires great labor and persistence, they carry their families usually along with them."

Actually, there are two animals living in Arctic waters that do yield a kind of ivory, and obviously Father Avril was thinking of one or both of these. One is the walrus, a relative of the seal, which bears two large tusks that may reach a length of two or three feet. The other is the narwhal, a curious species of whale that seems to have a single long horn jutting from its forehead. The narwhal's "horn" is really a tooth; the animal has only two teeth, and the left one undergoes a strange development in adult male narwhals, sprouting through the upper lip and growing to a length of seven or eight feet.

The tusk of the narwhal winds in a spiral twist for its entire length, and could not possibly be mistaken for an elephant's tusk. The tusk of a walrus does look something like the tusk of an elephant, although walrus tusks are much smaller. Those who could not believe in Siberian elephants preferred to think, as Father Avril did, that the ivory came from the walrus or some other aquatic creature.

Of course, the Siberian natives themselves knew that the ivory for which they had such a ready market came neither from the walrus nor the narwhal; and they also knew nothing about elephants. The ivory came out of the ground. The tales they told about the animal that produced it were similar to the old Chinese legends of a giant rat living in the earth.

Some of these folk tales came to the attention of European travelers in Siberia. One of them was Evert Ysbrant Ides, a Dutch diplomat in the service of Peter the Great, Czar of Russia. In 1692, the Czar sent Ides to China to conclude a treaty with the Emperor K'ang-hsi. Ides' route took him through Siberia, where he took the opportunity to do some research on the ivory from the Arctic. He talked to members of three Mongol tribes of Siberia, the Yakuts, the Ostiaks, and the Tunguses, and they told him stories about a giant rat that they called *mamantu* or *mammut,* which Ides thought meant "that-which-lives-beneath-the-ground." Ides wrote that the *mammut* lives in tunnels, going to and fro in the earth. "They further believe," he said, "that if this animal comes near the surface of the frozen earth so as to smell or discern the air, he immediately dies. This is the reason that several of them are found dead on the high banks of the rivers, where they accidentally come out of the ground."

Ides also obtained information of a somewhat

more reliable sort from one of his traveling companions, a Russian whose business it was to trade in this *mammut* ivory. Using the facts this man gave him, Ides wrote:

"Amongst the hills which are situated northeast of, and not far from here [the Siberian village of Makofskoy], the *mammut*'s tongues and legs are found; as they are also particularly on the shores of the Rivers Jenize, Trugan, Mongamsea, Lena, and near Jakutskoi, to as far as the Frozen Sea. In the spring when the ice of this river breaks, it is driven in such vast quantities, and with such force by the high swollen waters, that it frequently carries very high banks before it, and breaks off the tops of hills, which, falling down, reveal these animals whole, or their teeth only, almost frozen to the earth, which thaw by degrees. I had a person with me to China, who annually went out in search of these bones; he told me as a certain truth, that he and his companions found a head of one of these animals, which was discovered by the fall of such a frozen piece of earth. As soon as he opened it he found the greatest part of the flesh rotten, but it was not without difficulty that they broke out his teeth, which were placed before his mouth as those of the elephants are; they also took some bones out of his head, and afterwards came to his fore-foot, which they cut off, and carried part of it to the city of Trugan, the circumference being as large as that of the waist of an ordinary man. The bones of the head appeared somewhat red, as though they were tinctured with blood."

Curious about these monstrous ivory-bearing

beasts hidden in the frozen ground, Ides questioned a number of Siberians of Russian ancestry, knowing that they would not share the fantastic beliefs of the Mongol tribesmen about giant underground rats. These Siberians told Ides "that the *mammut* is very like the elephant; with this only difference, that the teeth [tusks] of the former are firmer, and not so straight as those of the latter."

The first account of Ides' travels appeared in a book called *North and East Tartary,* by Cornelius Witzen. Like Ides, Witzen was Dutch; he had visited Moscow in 1666, and in 1694 he published a book that described not only his own travels but those of several other men, including Ides. Witzen's book was the first to print the word "mammoth," or something close to it. He described how a great many tusks are found on the banks of the Siberian rivers, and noted, "By the Inlanders [the Russian settlers in Siberia] these teeth are called *mammout-tekoos,* while the animal itself is called *mammout.*"

In 1697 another account of Ides' journey was printed, this the work of Adam Brand, his private secretary. Ides' own narrative finally was published in a Dutch edition in 1704, in an English translation in 1706, and in German in 1707. It was extremely popular among European readers and was reissued in several forms in the first half of the eighteenth century.

Ides' book should have settled the controversy over Siberian ivory. The Russian settlers had given him a clear and sensible explanation: this *mammut* was an elephant-like beast that had lived before the Deluge, when Siberia for some reason was warm enough to permit such creatures to survive. But though Ides' traveling companion claimed to have seen the frozen head and foot of one of these creatures, Ides himself had not beheld such things. It was as easy to believe in giant ground-dwelling rats with tusks as it was to believe in frozen elephants, anyway, and even easier to think that the Siberian ivory came from the walrus. So the matter remained unresolved even after Ides' book came out.

Nearly every European who visited Siberia tried to learn something about the perplexing ivory and the animal from which it came. In 1715, Peter the Great once again sent a Dutch diplomat to the court of the Emperor K'ang-hsi. His name was Lorenz Lange. The route he took led him through Siberia. In the journal of his travels that was published in 1722, Lange wrote, "In the neighborhood of this place [the town of Jeniseisk] and further down towards Mangasea, are found a strange sort of bones like ivory, along the banks of the river, and in the hollows occasioned by the fall of the earth. Many of the inhabitants are of opinion, that they are actually elephant bones, which were carried thither by the Deluge. Others maintain they are no real bones, teeth, etc., but a species of *cornu fossile* [fossil horn] that grows in the earth. Some again give out, that a monstrous great beast lives underground, which they call *maman,* which cannot endure either air or light; they pretend it has a great horn on the forehead, with which it throws up the earth before it, and which is the abovesaid bone resembling an elephant's tooth, that is found in Siberia."

Lange believed that the *maman* must still exist,

for "many credible persons averred to me, that they themselves had seen horns, jawbones and ribs of it, with fresh blood and flesh sticking to it." But he did not see such things himself.

Maman, mammut, mammout, mamantu—what kind of animal was it? Russian traders went on buying its tusks in Siberia and selling them to foreigners under the name of *mamontova-kosty,* "mamont ivory," but its origin remained hidden in folklore and mystery.

A great deal of information about this mysterious beast reached the western world shortly after Lange's journey, as a by-product of a complicated struggle known as the Great Northern War, which broke out in 1700 when several of Sweden's neighbors decided that the Scandinavian kingdom's power was growing too great. Saxony, Denmark, and Russia attacked Sweden in separate thrusts, but Sweden's heroic young King Charles XII led an able defense, and soon was carrying the war to his enemies' territory. In 1707, Charles marched an army of 40,000 men deep into Russia. But like everyone else who has ever tried to invade Russia, he found the task too great, and in July, 1709, his army was crushed by the forces of Czar Peter the Great. The Swedish king managed to escape, but about 3,000 of his men were captured, including many officers.

The Swedes were not treated harshly. They were, in fact, allowed to do whatever and go wherever they pleased, so long as they did not leave Siberia. A number of the captive officers were educated, cultivated men of scholarly and inquisitive natures, and they chose to pass their time carrying out useful investigations. Some of them explored the bleak northern wastelands; others studied the customs of the native tribes; still others set up schools to teach the primitive tribesmen mathematics, science, and European languages. When Peter the Great heard what his prisoners were doing, he was both surprised and pleased, and encouraged them to continue. The Czar commissioned the Swedish officers to travel everywhere in Siberia at the expense of the Russian government, making maps, collecting specimens of animal and plant life, and carrying out surveys of this virtually unknown territory.

Among these energetic Swedish prisoners was a captain named Johann Bernhard Müller, who devoted himself to a study of the Ostiaks, one of the Mongol tribes of Siberia. He compiled a report on the Ostiaks that he sent to the Russian capital of St. Petersburg, and somehow it shortly found its way to western Europe, where it was published in German in 1720 and in English two years later. One of the most interesting sections of Müller's essay, "The Manners and Customs of the Ostiaks," began with these words:

> There is a curiosity in Siberia, nowhere else to be met with in any part of the world, for ought I know. This is what the inhabitants call *mamant*, which is found in the earth in several places. It looks like ivory both as to color and grain. . . .

Müller considered the three main explanations which had been offered to account for the presence of this substance in the ground—that it comes from the tusks of antediluvian elephants, that it is some sort of mineral that happens to take the shape of tusks, and that it is the horn of a strange beast which lives underground. None of the three appealed to him.

"The notion that these bones are real elephants' teeth," he wrote, "cannot be supported by any probable argument, considering that elephants are utterly unknown in those parts, nor could they subsist in that cold climate, if they were carried thither. And yet these teeth or horns are mostly met with in the coldest places of Siberia."

The idea that the tusks were natural minerals, like coal or rocksalt, was even less acceptable. Müller destroyed it altogether with an argument based on simple experience: "For it is observed that many times such horns have been found all bloody at the broken end, which is generally hollow, and filled with a matter like concreted blood. Besides, they often find skulls and jawbones with molar teeth or grinders in them of a prodigious size. . . . I myself, and several of my fellow-prisoners, have often seen such teeth, one of which weighed twenty or twenty-four pounds and better."

But Müller was also uncomfortable with the third theory, that of the underground beast—mainly because he could obtain no reliable proof that such a creature existed. He wrote, "Some think that they [the tusks] are the horns of a live huge beast, which lives in marshes and underground caves, feeding on the mud and carving a way for itself with its horns through the mirc and earth; but when it chances to meet with a sandy place, the sands press round it so much, that because of its bulk it cannot get free, and sticks fast at last and perishes. I have spoken with many persons, who assured me sincerely that beyond the Beresovka River they saw such beasts in the caves of the high mountains there. According to these descriptions they are enormous, being four or five yards high, and three fathoms in length. They are gray in color, with a long head, broad forehead, and two horns on each side just above the two eyes. They can move these horns and cross them one over the other when they wish. In walking they are said to be able to stretch themselves to a great length, and also to contract themselves into a short span. Their legs are about the same size as those of a bear.'' Müller added, though, that one does not know how far to rely on such stories, since the natives that tell them are not skilled in careful observation, and are only curious about things that might be profitable.

Another of the Swedish prisoners who sought information about the *mammut* was Baron Philipp Johann Tabbert von Strahlenberg, whose important work on the geography of Russia and Siberia saw print in 1730, after his return from captivity. Before that, though, he sent back to Europe what seemed like an important scientific contribution: a sketch of a *mammut*.

Strahlenberg had been asked by Peter the Great

to survey a large section of Siberia, and in the course of this work he had heard all the usual tales about tusk-bearing rats of great size. One Russian whom he met claimed to have seen the *mammut* and could draw a picture of it. Strahlenberg accepted the sketch, and, when one of his fellow-prisoners named Baron Kagg was released in 1722, he gave the drawing to Kagg to take back to Sweden.

The picture Kagg brought home did not portray any kind of burrowing animal. It showed a creature that looked something like an ox with a long, tufted tail. But it had claws more fierce than any tiger's; and from its forehead there sprouted two long horns that twisted several times around one another. Kagg insisted that monsters of this kind still roamed the Siberian tundra, and that he and Strahlenberg had seen their horns buried under the ice.

Strahlenberg's other contribution to the lore of the mammoth—to use the form of the name that won general use—had to do with the origin of its name. Ides had claimed that *mamantu* or *mammut* means "that-which-lives-beneath-the-ground" in some Siberian language, while other travelers had thought that the word in its various forms (*mamant, maman,* and so forth) meant something like "large," or that it came from *mama,* supposedly a Mongol word for "earth." But the fact that so many different derivations were offered cast doubt on all of them, and no one really knew where the word had come from.

Strahlenberg argued that "mammoth" was merely a Russian way of pronouncing "mehemot," which he said was the word used for the ivory-bearing creature by the Arab traders who visited Siberia. And "mehemot," Strahlenberg went on, was the Arab pronunciation of the Hebrew word "behemoth," meaning "a large animal." Through this process of mispronunciation a beast out of the Bible lent its name to the tusked mystery of the Siberian icefields.

The behemoth is a monster described in the 40th chapter of the Book of Job, in which God tells Job:

> Behold behemoth, which I made as I made you;
>   he eats grass like an ox.
> Behold, his strength in his loins, and his power
>   in the muscles of his belly.
> He makes his tail stiff like a cedar; the sinews
>   of his thighs are knit together.
> His bones are tubes of bronze, his limbs like
>   bars of iron.

Certainly a frightening creature! And certainly the Arabs who came to Siberia could have been familiar with the Book of Job and its behemoth, which they called the "mehemot." Using the same name for the Siberian beast would be reasonable enough, and from "mehemot" to "mammut" is no great journey for a word to travel.

The trouble with Strahlenberg's clever argument is that the Book of Job gives a few additional details about the behemoth that permit it to be identified as an animal quite different from the ivory-bearing giant of Siberia:

For the mountains yield food for him where
all the wild beasts play.
Under the lotus plants he lies, in the covert
of the reeds and in the marsh.
For his shade the lotus trees cover him;
the willows of the brook surround him.
Behold, if the river is turbulent he is
not frightened. . . .

This is a recognizable portrait of that bulky but peaceful creature of African rivers and lakes, the hippopotamus. Since the nineteenth century, scholars have believed that the Hebrew word "behemoth" is derived from an even older Egyptian word, "p-ehe-mau," which literally means "water ox"—or hippopotamus. Of course, it is still possible that the word "mammoth" may have evolved out of the word "behemoth" in the way Strahlenberg suggested, since "behemoth" has long been used to mean *any* big beast. In that sense, the Siberian mammoth was a behemoth, though not *the* behemoth of the Book of Job. However, the question of how the mammoth got its name is still unanswered, and probably will remain that way.

The research that Strahlenberg and the other Swedish prisoners were doing in Siberia so interested Czar Peter the Great that in 1723 he sent a German naturalist, Daniel Gottleib Messerschmidt, there to learn more about the mammoth. One of the first people Messerschmidt encountered in Siberia was a Russian, Michael Wolochowicz, who said that a mammoth had recently emerged from melting ice on the banks of the Indigirka River, which flows into the Arctic Ocean in eastern Siberia. A Russian soldier named Erlow had seen the animal's head jutting out of the ice, and soon, as the hot Siberian summer began, the whole animal was exposed. Unfortunately, wolves came to feed on the mammoth's flesh, and most of the meat they did not eat quickly rotted and decayed, so that by the time Wolochowicz reached the site not much was left of the animal except its skeleton. But he was able to make an important discovery on the opposite bank of the river. As he told Messerschmidt, "I saw a piece of skin putrefied, appearing out of the side of a sand-hill, which was pretty large, thick-set, and brown, somewhat resembling goat's hair; which skin I could not take for that of a goat, but of the behemoth, inasmuch as I could not appropriate it to any animal that I knew."

This strange specimen of skin, with its covering of coarse, woolly brown fur, seemed to be proof that mammoths must still exist somewhere in Siberia. But no one succeeded in sighting a live mammoth, and the report of a traveler named Khariton Laptev, who journeyed through northern Siberia from 1739 to 1743, indicated that the mammoths in the ground might be quite ancient, held in an everlasting deep freeze. Laptev wrote, "On the banks of several rivers on the tundra, whole mammoths with their tusks are dug out with thick hides on them. Their hair and bodies are, however, rotten, while the bones, except the tusks, are also decaying."

While scientists puzzled over the mysteries of the

mammoth, the ivory traders did an ever-increasing business in *mamontova-kosty*. Siberia seemed to be an immense storehouse of the precious ivory. In 1750 a merchant named Lyakhov came upon an unusually rich supply of mammoth bones near the Anadyr River, and this discovery touched off a treasure hunt covering much of Siberia. Lyakhov himself made the next major find in 1770 on two islands in the Laptev Sea, a part of the Arctic Ocean named for the earlier explorer. These two islands—now called the Lyakhov Islands—must once have been occupied by vast herds of mammoths. In summertime, Lyakhov found, the melting of the ice exposed heaps of mammoth bones and tusks, along with the remains of other large animals. One of the islands almost seemed paved with bones. Hot weather caused the muddy banks of lakes and rivers to split open, revealing immense bones that stuck out of the ground. Lyakhov built huts and brought in workmen to help him "mine" the ivory. Three years later, he found an equally rich supply of fossils on the island group just to the north, known today as the New Siberian Islands. For a long while he kept news of his finds secret so that others would not plunder his source of ivory.

The amount of fossil ivory that Lyakhov and others like him uncovered was incredible. One ivory-hunter of the early nineteenth century brought back 20,000 pounds of ivory—more than 150 great tusks —in a single year. The town of Yakutsk was the chief marketplace where the ivory was sold; an average of 50,000 pounds of ivory a year went on sale in Yakutsk throughout the nineteenth century, meaning that the remains of several hundred mammoths must have been discovered annually. All during the nineteenth century the volume of trade in mammoth relics grew steadily. In 1872, 1630 mammoth tusks were placed on sale in London by ivory dealers; in 1873, 1140 more tusks were sold. The tusks of perhaps 50,000 mammoths were unearthed and marketed in the nineteenth century alone.

Though the flow of ivory out of Siberia was immense, the flow of scientific information about the source of that ivory was scanty indeed. As late as 1800, no one outside Siberia and Russia had any clear idea what kind of animal yielded the ivory. It might be a walrus, it might be an elephant, it might be some fantastic underground rat—who could say?

If someone who knew anything about natural history had had a chance to see a freshly thawed Siberian mammoth as it emerged from the ice, he would have been able to identify it as a kind of elephant—a weird and hairy elephant, to be sure, but undoubtedly an elephant. However, the scientists who toured Russia in the eighteenth century had to depend on second-hand stories.

The merchants who marketed the ivory must have known the nature of the beast from which it came, but they kept quiet, trying to preserve the secrecy of the best sites. And the men who dug the ivory from Siberia's mud, the Mongol tribesmen themselves, were not scientists, and they had no interest in classifying or studying old bones, only in selling them. In fact, they had a superstitious fear of mammoths that prevented them from examining the beasts too closely. They were happy enough to find tusks lying in a jumbled heap of bones, or sticking out of the ground. But now and then they would come upon the body of a complete mammoth that had been preserved, skin and all, in Siberia's deep freeze. These the tribesmen avoided. They believed that mammoths were creatures of the underground world, the dark realm of demons and ghosts. It was bad luck to meddle with such creatures. The Siberians felt that death would soon come to the man who disturbed a mammoth, and to all his family as well.

So the European scientists trying to solve the mystery of the "giants' bones" were deprived of news from the one part of the world where not only the bones, but even the skin and the hair, of the "giants" were being found. Still, they made considerable progress during the eighteenth century in understanding what kind of bones they were that had been discovered in Europe so frequently.

The leading authority on Europe's giant fossil bones was Johann Friedrich Blumenbach, a professor of medicine at the University of Göttingen in Germany. He had collected many of these bones himself, and he had also traveled widely, seeking out and examining the "giants' bones" that were on display as curios in so many European churches, universities, and city halls. In 1799, after a lengthy study of this material, Blumenbach announced that the fossils were—as many other scientists had said —those of elephants. But, he added, the fossil elephants of Europe were of a type different from the living elephants found in Africa and Asia.

Difference between modern Asian
and African elephants

It was already well known that African elephants differed in many ways from Asian ones. The African elephants had bigger ears, longer tusks, and fewer ribs, to name just a few of many differences. Blumenbach showed that the fossil elephants had skeletons that varied greatly in structure from those of both African *and* Asian elephants. He regarded them as a species apart from the living types—an ancient form, an early model, so to speak. Blumenbach gave the fossil elephant the scientific name of *Elephas primigenius,* "first-born elephant."

He did not know, however, how different from living elephants his "first-born" type really was. Blumenbach would have needed to see one of Siberia's frozen mammoths for that. Then he would have realized that the fossil elephant of Europe and the puzzling underground giant of Siberia were the same— a strange animal out of the distant past.

In August, 1799, just about the time that Blumenbach was publishing his theories about *Elephas primigenius,* a scientific specimen that would have been useful in his studies was discovered on the shores of the Arctic Ocean. A Tungus chief named Ossip Shumakhov, searching for ivory along a creek in the delta of the Lena River, spied something dark and large inside a huge block of ice. He did not know what it was, although its shape seemed unusual to him. When he passed the same way again in 1800, he peered once more at the block of ice, which had thawed a little since the previous year. Now it seemed to Shumakhov that some great animal was encased in the ice, but he could get only a distorted and unclear view of it.

Shumakhov returned to the creek in the Lena delta in 1801, and this time there was no doubt about what he saw. Within the block of ice lay the carcass of a mammoth. The side of the animal and one long tusk protruded into the open.

The sight of the monster gave Shumakhov no pleasure. He was a superstitious man, and knew of the terrible fate supposed to come to anyone who touched or even looked at a mammoth carcass. Just a few years before, a man he knew had fallen ill and died shortly after making just such a discovery, and his family soon had followed him to the grave. Shumakhov hurried away, shielding his eyes from the dangerous creature and wondering uncomfortably if he had already been too close to it.

Then he became sick, and was convinced that the mammoth had destroyed him. He lay weakly on his deathbed, wishing he had never gone near the thing. But, to his own great surprise, his health returned; and once he was well again, Shumakhov found that he had been cured not only of his disease but of his superstitious fear of mammoths. The beast had not killed him after all, and its tusks were valuable; why not make some money out of it? In the summer of 1803 he went back to the mammoth. That was an unusually hot summer in Siberia, and the block of ice was completely gone; the mammoth lay fully exposed beside the creek. Shumakhov started to cut off its tusks, but his nerve failed him, and again he fled.

A Russian dealer in *mamontova-kosty*, one Roman Boltunov, appeared in the neighborhood, offering a good price for ivory. In March, 1804, Shumakhov told Boltunov about the thawed mammoth, and the trader talked him into showing him the beast. They went to the site together and pried loose the tusks, for which Boltunov paid the Siberian the sum of 50 rubles. Boltunov also made a sketch of the animal's carcass and one of its molar teeth.

Two years later, Mikhail Ivanovich Adams, a botanist who taught at the Academy of Sciences in St. Petersburg, paid a visit to the Siberian town of Yakutsk, the center of the ivory trade. While he was there he heard about Shumakhov's mammoth and obtained the drawing Boltunov had made. Adams sent the sketch to the Academy of Sciences and set out at once to salvage whatever might be left of the carcass. With him went Shumakhov and a group of Russian and Siberian merchants and ivory-hunters.

They found the mammoth in bad shape. Wolves, foxes, and bears had gnawed its flesh. A few of the braver natives had allowed their dogs to feed on it. The side of the mammoth that faced upward had been reduced to little more than a skeleton. One of the forelegs was gone altogether, probably ripped off by wolves; the trunk was also gone. But the immense skull was still covered with skin, and one shaggy ear was intact. So was the left eye and most of the mammoth's brain. The side on which the animal was lying was almost undamaged; the dark gray hide was there, covered with thick reddish hair, and hundreds of pounds of meat and fat remained in place.

Adams and his helpers had to cut the colossal beast up in order to ship it to Russia. It was no simple job; the hide, after it had been separated from the skeleton, was so heavy that it took ten men to lift it. Nearly all of the mammoth's hair fell off when the carcass was moved, but Adams carefully gathered it up—thirty-seven pounds of it—and packed it in a crate. He also packed the inch-thick hide after boiling it to dispose of the fat attached to it. The ankle of the right foreleg, the sole of that foot, and the head, all with skin on them, were left in their original state. Everything was loaded aboard sleds and hauled to the river to be shipped to Yakutsk, where Adams succeeded in purchasing the mammoth's tusks from Boltunov. Then he sent his treasure to the Academy of Sciences in St. Petersburg. It caused such a stir that the Academy decided to buy it from Professor Adams, giving him 8,000 rubles for it—160 times as much as Ossip Shumakhov had received for the tusks. The skeleton was mounted and placed on exhibit in the Academy's museum of zoology, and it can be seen there to this day in the city of Leningrad, as St. Petersburg now is known.

The sketch Boltunov had made of the thawed mammoth was forwarded by the Academy of Sciences to the German expert on fossil elephants, Professor Blumenbach. At last Blumenbach was able to get some idea of how his "first-born elephant" looked in the flesh. He could not get a very good idea, though, since Boltunov's sketch was hardly a masterpiece: the mammoth had already lost its trunk when he first saw it, the pressure of the ice had pushed the tusks out at weird angles, and he had mistaken the ear-holes for the mammoth's eye-sock-

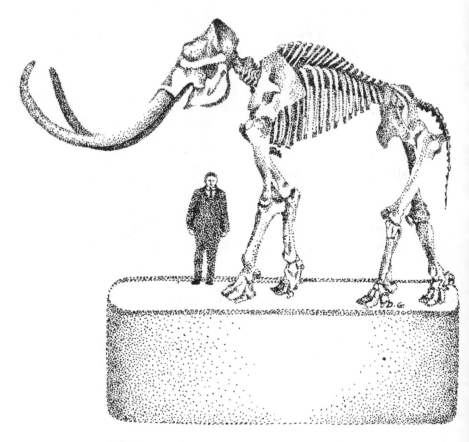

Skeleton of a mammoth compared with man

ets. The result was that the drawing seemed to depict some kind of massive giant pig with long pillar-like legs and two enormous tusks thrusting out at right angles to its body. Still, it was a good attempt, considering that the mammoth had not been in perfect condition and that Boltunov had probably never seen any kind of elephant before.

Blumenbach gladly made allowances for the drawing's flaws. He was delighted by the discovery, which confirmed so much that he had asserted. He wrote in German on the bottom of the drawing, "*Elephas primigenius,* which in Russia is called *mammut,* dug up with skin and hair in 1806 at the mouth of the Lena River at the Ice Ocean. Badly drawn, just as it was found, mutilated and all dirty."

The truth was clear now. Europe and Siberia once had been inhabited by elephants, strange hairy elephants that must have been capable of tolerating bitterly cold weather. No one would talk of "giants' bones" any longer. But the theories of Blumenbach and the skeleton brought back from Siberia by Adams raised more questions than they answered. Had Europe once had the same sort of climate as Siberia? How could the climate of a region change so drastically? Why was it that mammoths were found only as skeletons in Europe, but as complete carcasses in Siberia? Did they still survive in Siberia, as the natives claimed? In that case, why had they vanished from Europe? Was Noah's Deluge to blame for the disappearance of the mammoths? If so, how could the Deluge somehow have missed Siberia?

And what if the mammoths were extinct everywhere? Why had they died out? Did they perish in the Deluge, or was there some other reason? Was it *possible* for an entire species to die out? Why would God destroy a whole type of animal?

Man knew very little about the past, that much was evident. The riddle of the mammoths demanded a solution. But before anyone would be able to say when it had been that elephants had lived in Europe, and why it was that they had disappeared, a tremendous scientific and philosophical revolution would have to occur, shaking accepted beliefs apart and opening new and frightening paths to understanding.

CHAPTER THREE

BEHEMOTH IN THE NEW WORLD

While European scientists were debating the problem of the fossil elephants in the eighteenth century, a somewhat similar discussion was arising in America, where elephant fossils had also been discovered. The main difference was that Europe had been fully explored and settled centuries ago; everyone knew that no wild elephants were found there, and so the fossils raised the problem of the extinction of a species. In the New World, though, the elephant might not necessarily be extinct. Nobody had ever seen one wandering about in the Thirteen Colonies, but it was altogether possible that the unknown land west of the Appalachians might contain as many live elephants as Africa. So the discovery of fossil elephant bones in North America did not at first create the sort of philosophical difficulties that were presented by the discovery of such bones in England or France.

Cortés and his men, as we have already seen, encountered fossil elephant bones in 1519 during their invasion of Mexico. But of course at that time such bones were regarded as the remains of giant men who had lived before the Deluge. When tremendous bones and teeth were found in New York State in 1705, these, too, were considered to be the relics of giants.

Appropriately, some Negro slaves who had recently been brought from Africa were the first to identify the big bones correctly as those of elephants. The English naturalist Mark Catesby, writing in 1743 concerning some fossils that had been found about ten years earlier, said:

"At a place in Carolina called Stono, was dug out of the Earth three or four Teeth of a large Animal, which, by the concurring Opinion of all the Negroes, native Africans, that saw them, were the Grinders of an Elephant, and in my Opinion they could be no other; I having seen some of the like that are brought from Africa."

Fossils of a similar kind started to come to light in North America with some frequency, particularly after explorers began to move out past the Appalachians into the interior of the continent. No one now questioned their identity as elephant bones.

One important discovery was made in 1739 by the Baron de Longueuil, an officer in the French army. Longueuil was ordered to lead a force of French and

Indian troops from Montreal to Louisiana, where the Chickasaw Indians were causing trouble. Part of the way he traveled along the Ohio River, and in the summer of 1739, while camping in a marsh somewhere near the present site of Louisville, Kentucky, he came upon a deposit of large bones and teeth, which he believed were elephant fossils. Longueuil collected a tusk, a thighbone, and several molars. He took them to France with him in 1740 and they passed into the possession of the Jardin du Roi, the royal zoo and museum. They were the first fossil bones from America to undergo serious scientific study in Europe, and, as we shall see, created some complications for the scholars a few decades later.

Not far from Longueuil's discovery site—the actual location of which is unknown today—an even richer source of fossils came to light in the middle of the eighteenth century. This was Big Bone Lick, in what is now Boone County, Kentucky, southwest of Covington. Here a salty spring flowed from the ground; animals had come to lick the salt, and some of them, becoming mired in the marshy soil, had been buried in mud and died. In 1751, a traveler named Christopher Gist visited that part of Kentucky and was given two large fossil teeth that a settler had found at Big Bone Lick. The settler said that huge bones and teeth covered an entire valley there, some half buried in the bog, others exposed by the action of rain and streams. A good many such bones were carried away as souvenirs. By 1762 John Bartram of Philadelphia, one of America's most famous naturalists, heard of the Kentucky bones and asked his friend James Wright to check the truth of the stories.

Wright consulted a pair of Shawnee Indians who lived near the salt lick. Yes, they had seen bones there, including, Wright said in a letter to Bartram, "the remains of 5 entire skeletons, with their heads all pointing towards each other, and near together, supposed to have fallen at the same time." The skulls of these animals were so large that a man could barely clasp his arms around them, and the shoulder blades, when stood on end, were as tall as a man. They had tusks ten or twelve feet long, and, Wright said, "they judged the creature when alive must have been the size of a small house." Many other such skeletons were scattered around in that region.

Had any of these big animals ever been seen alive, Wright wanted to know? "They answered," he told Bartram, "they had never heard them spoken of, other than as in the condition they are at present, nor ever heard of any such creature having been seen by the oldest man, or his father." The Shawnees did have a tradition that long ago there had been men as big as the great beasts, who hunted them, slew them, and slung them over their backs "as an Indian now does a deer." But, said the Shawnees, "when there were no more of these strong men left alive, God killed these mighty creatures, that they should not hurt the present race of Indians."

The first man to excavate the Big Bone Lick fossils in anything like a scientific way was an Irishman named George Croghan, who had left Dublin for the wilds of Pennsylvania in 1741. Croghan won the friendship of the Indians of the Ohio Valley, and became wealthy by setting up a chain of trading posts throughout the area. He played an important role in the British victory in the French and Indian War, by which France lost control of much of her North American territory. After the war, Croghan was sent into the Ohio Valley to gain support for the British among the Indians, and while on this journey he came to Big Bone Lick on May 30, 1765.

Collecting fossils had long been one of Croghan's hobbies, and he made good use of his time at Big Bone Lick, which he called in his diary "the place where the elephants' bones are found." He noted, "It appears that there are vast quantities of these bones lying five or six feet underground, which we discovered in the bank, at the edge of the Lick. We found here two tusks above six feet long; we carried one, with some other bones, to our boats, and set off. . . ."

About a week later Croghan's party was attacked by Indians. Five of his men were killed; the others and Croghan himself were captured. The fossils he had collected were lost when the Indians carried him off. After some months as a prisoner, Croghan was freed, and in July, 1766, he returned to Big Bone Lick and succeeded in taking away a good many fossils.

He wanted to know more about these bones than anyone in the United States could tell him, and so he sent a few specimens to Europe. Two tusks, several molar teeth, and a jawbone went to Lord Shelburne, the British statesman who was in charge of administering the colonies in America; Shelburne was friendly with many of Britain's most prominent scientists, and Croghan hoped he could obtain some information from them about the fossils. Croghan also sent three molars, six tusks, and a rib to an American of scientific inclinations who happened to be living in London just then—Benjamin Franklin.

To Franklin, Croghan's gift was a package of fascinating, tantalizing mysteries. On August 5, 1767, he sent this reply to Croghan:

"I return you many thanks for the box of elephants' tusks and grinders. They are extremely curious on many accounts; no living elephants having been seen in any part of America by any of the Europeans settled there, or remembered in any tradition of the Indians. It is also puzzling to conceive what should have brought so many of them to die on the same spot; and that no such remains should be found in any other part of the continent, except in that very distant country, Peru, from whence some grinders of the same kind, formerly brought, are now in the museum of the Royal Society. The tusks agree with those of the African and Asiatic elephant in being nearly of the same form and texture, and some of them, notwithstanding the length of time they must have lain, being still good ivory. But the grinders differ, being full of knobs, like the grinders of a carnivorous animal; when those of the elephant, who eats only vegetables, are almost smooth. But then we know of no other animal with tusks like an elephant, to whom such grinders might belong.

"It is remarkable, that elephants now inhabit naturally only hot countries where there is no winter, and yet these remains are found in a winter country; and it is no uncommon thing to find elephants' tusks in Siberia, in great quantities, when their rivers overflow, and wash away the earth, though Siberia is still more a wintry country than that on the Ohio; which looks as if the earth had anciently been in another position, and the climates differently placed from what they are at present."

Franklin's letter takes up many of the problems that the fossil elephants had caused for scientists. He seems willing to believe that these elephants are extinct, though he does not understand why they have died out. He offers one brilliant suggestion, far ahead of his time, when he says that perhaps the world once was tipped at a different angle on its axis, so that lands now arctic were tropic then, and vice versa. This is certainly an ingenious explanation for the presence of elephants in Siberia. It does not happen to be the correct one, but it interestingly foreshadows a twentieth-century· theory, now the subject of great controversy, which suggests that at several times in the past the Earth's position *has* changed, creating vast shifts in climate.

Franklin raises another important point when he takes up the problem of the teeth. Living elephants have large oblong teeth whose crowns, or grinding faces, are virtually flat. Across the crowns runs a series of alternating ridges: narrow white ridges of hard enamel, separated by wider ridges of a dull-colored cement-like substance. An African elephant has ten or eleven of these cross-ridges; an Asian elephant has twenty-seven. The enamel ridges stand out a fraction of an inch above the rest of the crown. When the animals chew the branches, leaves, vines, and grass that are their preferred foods, they move their lower jaws back and forth so that what they are eating is ground between the two sets of tooth-ridges as though between two rough grindstones.

The mammoth fossils found in Europe and in Siberia had essentially the same kind of molars. The pattern of ridges was slightly different, but the arrangement was similar enough so that anyone who had seen an elephant's tooth would know that the mammoth must have been closely related to modern elephants. The fossil teeth seen by the Negro slaves in Carolina in the early eighteenth century were also flat, ridged grinders, easily recognizable as coming from some type of elephant; evidently there had been mammoths in the New World too.

But the teeth that George Croghan sent to Benjamin Franklin were altogether different. Instead of having many narrow cross-ridges, their crowns bore several large knobby projections, two to three inches high. Also, the roots of the teeth were long prongs, while the roots of the teeth of elephants and mammoths are small. These Big Bone Lick teeth were not flat grinders at all; they were jagged and bumpy, like giant versions of our own back teeth. To Franklin it seemed quite possible that such teeth had belonged to a meat-eating animal. And elephants are strictly vegetarians.

Several European scholars had already tackled the puzzle of the teeth from the New World, without much success. In 1756 the French geologist Jean Guettard published an essay in which he discussed certain fossils from North America and compared them with fossils found in Europe. Among the specimens he examined were the bones and teeth that the Baron de Longueuil had found in Kentucky and brought to France in 1740. Guettard remarked that the tusk and the thighbone Longueuil had collected were not very different from those of elephants, living or fossil. But the molar teeth were baffling. He provided a drawing of one, showing its long roots and the nine gnarled knobs on its crown. ''What animal is this?'' he asked, but he could not answer his own question.

In 1762, Louis Jean Daubenton, the curator of natural history at the Jardin du Roi, offered what sounded like a sensible explanation: the tusk and thighbone Longueuil had found came from an elephant, but the gnarled molar belonged to a large hippopotamus! To prove his point, Daubenton compared the Kentucky thighbone in the Jardin du Roi's collection with the thighbone of a recent elephant and the thighbone of a Siberian mammoth. The structure of all three was similar, though the fossil bones were much thicker and sturdier than the recent one. Daubenton argued that the three animals must all be classed in the same species. He was one of the first scientists to claim that the Siberian mammoth was related to the elephant, something that Johann Blumenbach would make absolutely clear thirty-five years later. Obviously, then, said Daubenton, the teeth found near the Kentucky thighbone must have come from some other animal, since they were totally unlike elephant teeth; and he showed that they were fairly similar to the teeth of the hippopotamus.

It was a logical solution, but it happened to be incorrect. Daubenton had not had enough information to go by, since the only American fossils available to him were the scattered bones and teeth Longueuil had found. In 1767, though, George Croghan's cases of fossils arrived in London. They included many more bones of the elephant-like beasts, discovered not far from the place where Longueuil had obtained his. And among them was a definitely elephant-like jawbone that still contained two of the gnarled hippopotamus-like teeth!

The first English scientist to comment on the new finds was Peter Collinson, who examined the specimens Croghan had shipped to Lord Shelburne. On November 26, 1767, Collinson lectured on the fossils before the Royal Society, England's chief scientific body. The tusks from Big Bone Lick, said Collinson, are those of elephants, but, he went on, "It is very remarkable, and worthy of observation, none of the molars, or grinding teeth of elephants, are discovered with these tusks; but great numbers of very large pronged teeth of some vast animals are only found with them, which have no resemblance to the molars, or grinding teeth, of any great animal yet known." Collinson was not yet able to explain this. Nor could he understand how elephants had ever been able to survive in the Ohio Valley's climate. Perhaps the elephant fossils found in Europe, Siberia, and North America had been swept there from warmer lands by the waves of the Deluge, he suggested.

At the next meeting of the Royal Society, on December 10, 1767, Collinson took up the question of the puzzling teeth once more. He had carefully compared the Big Bone Lick tusks with those of African and Asian elephants and was even more positive than before that the fossils were those of elephants. But since the teeth were different from those of known species of elephant, Collinson said, ''I must conclude that they, with the long teeth [tusks] belong to another species of elephant, not yet known; or else that they are the remains of some vast animal that hath the long teeth, or tusks, of the elephant, with large grinders peculiar to that species, being different in size and shape from any animal yet known. . . .''

Collinson was entering dangerous ground with such statements. His words implied that the elephant-like creature with the strange teeth might be extinct, since no one in America had reported seeing a living one. But in the eighteenth century the idea that animals could become extinct was still highly unpopular. It violated the accepted religious teachings, for the churches still insisted that whatever God had created would survive unchanged until the Day of Judgment. One way around this was to say that the possessor of the knobby teeth had been an antediluvian animal that failed to get aboard Noah's Ark. But by Collinson's time few serious-minded scientists really took the Ark story seriously. They knew that the world was full of creatures, thousands upon thousands of different types, which could never have all been crammed aboard a single vessel, even two by two. They also knew that the animals of Africa were very different from the animals of the Americas, and those of Europe were unlike those of Asia, and so on around the world. If all creatures had come forth at the same time from one Ark, how was it that each corner of the world had its own special sorts of beasts?

Even those who paid little heed to the tales of the Bible, though, hesitated to claim that extinction was possible. To the philosophical-minded, it seemed somehow improper for a species to die out. Such thinkers believed in a "great chain of being," in which the universe is seen as a series of "links," running from inanimate objects up through simple living things to man, the angels, and God himself. This belief satisfied the eighteenth-century philosopher's love of order, harmony, and organized design. Take away any link in the chain, though—remove one animal, declare it extinct—and the harmony would shatter, the design would collapse into chaos.

Daubenton, faced with the possibility that Longueuil's fossils might come from an extinct animal, had shied away, insisting that the inexplicable teeth must be those of a hippopotamus. Collinson, though correctly seeing that the teeth and the elephant-like bones went together, also avoided the idea of extinction by putting forth the hope that the unknown animal must still exist somewhere in the New World.

"This great creature, to which these teeth belong, wherever it exists," Collinson said, "is probably supported by browsing on trees and shrubs, and other vegetable foods."

The famous British surgeon William Hunter, the foremost medical man of his day and an expert on anatomy, also examined the bones Croghan had shipped to London. On February 25, 1768, Hunter reported on his findings to the Royal Society. He had consulted professional carvers of ivory, who told him that the tusks from Big Bone Lick were "perfectly similar" to those of recent elephants. But by comparing the tooth-bearing lower jaw from Kentucky with the jaw of an elephant, Hunter showed in detail that the two animals had to belong to different species. The jaws themselves had roughly the same shape, but the difference of structure of the molars was extremely great. This was correct, though Hunter went astray in one detail. Like Franklin but unlike Collinson, he was deceived by the jaggedness of the Kentucky teeth's crowns into thinking that they came from a carnivorous animal.

In his final sentence, Hunter offered a conclusion which seems obvious to us, but which was startling and revolutionary in 1768: "And if this animal was indeed carnivorous, which I believe cannot be doubted, though we may as philosophers regret it, as men we cannot but thank Heaven that its whole generation is probably extinct." No one up till then had dared to say so publicly that these creatures no longer existed.

Benjamin Franklin, meanwhile, had altered some
of his thinking about the Kentucky animal in the
light of Peter Collinson's lecture of December, 1767.
In January, 1768, Franklin sent one of the teeth
from Croghan to his friend the Abbé Chappe
d'Auteroche, a noted French astronomer. Chappe
and Franklin had met in Paris in 1767. Franklin at
that time had spoken of the curious fossil teeth he
had lately received; Chappe, who had been to Siberia some years earlier and obtained mammoth teeth
there, asked to see one, and Franklin complied. In a
letter to Chappe of January 31, 1768, Franklin
offered some details about the tooth:

> It was found near the River Ohio in Amer-
> ica, about 200 leagues below Fort Du-
> quesne, at what is called the Great Lick-
> ing Place [Big Bone Lick], where the
> earth has a saltish taste that is agreeable
> to the buffaloes and deer, who come there
> at certain seasons in great number to lick
> the same. At this place have been found
> the skeletons of near 30 large animals sup-
> posed to be elephants, several tusks like
> those of elephants being found with these
> grinder teeth. . . . Some of our natural-
> ists here, however, contend that these are
> not the grinders of elephants but of some
> carnivorous animal unknown, because such
> knobs or prominences on the face of the
> tooth are not to be found on those of ele-
> phants, and only, as they say, on those of
> carnivorous animals. But it appears to me

that animals capable of carrying such
large heavy tusks, must themselves be
large creatures, too bulky to have the activity necessary for pursuing and taking
prey. . . .

Franklin thought that the knobby teeth represented
only a minor variation from the standard elephant-
tooth design.

It was now clear, at any rate, that the New World
contained at least two sorts of elephant fossil. One
was very much like the fossil elephants of Europe,
while the other had teeth of an unusual non-ele-
phant-like structure. But no one yet could say how
these fossil elephants were related to one another or
to the elephants of modern times; and no one could
say whether living specimens of the fossil types still
existed somewhere.

Among those who gave careful thought to these
matters was a certain Virginia gentleman named
Thomas Jefferson. Jefferson's wide-ranging mind
was attuned to many forms of learning; when not
engaged in public service he studied Indian lore, excavated prehistoric ruins, collected fossil bones, and
amused himself with astronomy, physics, mathematics, music, architecture, and a good deal besides.

Jefferson knew of the discoveries at Big Bone
Lick and of the various European theories about
fossil elephants. His own ideas about elephants and
mammoths, living and fossil, took form in the
1770's, when the available information on these sub-
jects was scanty and contradictory; thus Jefferson's

notions, while intelligently thought out, are full of errors. He believed that just two types of animals were involved in the whole controversy—mammoths and elephants. Elephants, he declared, were creatures that lived only in the torrid zones and had flat, ridged grinders. Mammoths were creatures of northern lands, with rows of rounded knobs on the crowns of their teeth. The fossil bones found at Big Bone Lick and other sites in the Ohio Valley were mammoth bones, Jefferson believed, and the Ohio animal was identical to the mammoth of Siberia. As for Daubenton's attempt to prove that the Ohio Valley bones belonged to an elephant and the grinders to a hippopotamus, Jefferson called it nonsense. He wrote:

Wherever these grinders are found, there also we find the tusks and skeleton; but no skeleton of the hippopotamus nor grinders of the elephant. It will not be said that the hippopotamus and elephant came always to the same spot, the former to deposit his grinders, and the latter his tusks and skeleton. For what became of the parts not deposited there? We must agree then that these remains belong to each other, that they are of one and the same animal, that this was not a hippopotamus, because the hippopotamus had no tusks nor such a frame, and because the grinders differ in their size as well as in the number and form of their points [from those of a hippopotamus].

Jefferson was right, of course, in saying that the knobby teeth and the elephant-like tusks belonged to the same animal. But he was wrong in calling that animal a mammoth. To Jefferson, mammoths were animals of great size whose remains had been found in Siberia, but it was impossible for him to know much more than that about the Siberian mammoths in 1781, the year Jefferson wrote the lines just quoted. A few travelers such as the Abbé Chappe had brought mammoth grinders back from Siberia, but detailed descriptions of them had not been published. So Jefferson did not realize that the mammoth of Siberia had flat, ridged grinders that were like those of an elephant and unlike those from Big Bone Lick. Whatever the Big Bone Lick animal was, it was not a mammoth.

Jefferson also failed to realize that there had been mammoths in Europe as well as in Siberia. He knew of the fossil elephants found in Europe, but he did not connect them with mammoths; he seems to have thought of them as creatures imported from Africa that had never lived wild in Europe. Not for almost a generation after Jefferson wrote his book was the truth realized. First, in 1799, Blumenbach showed that the fossil European elephants had skeletons different from those of tropical elephants, so that they deserved to be classed separately as *Elephas primigenius,* the "first-born elephant." Then, in 1806, when Adams emerged from Siberia with his complete mammoth skeleton, it became clear to scientists that Blumenbach's *Elephas primigenius,* whose fossils were found all over Europe, was identical with the mammoth of Siberia.

Lacking this information, Jefferson mistakenly tried to set up a sharp division between cold-weather animals (mammoths) and warm-weather animals (elephants). He thought that mammoths and elephants were quite different beasts. But the European fossil, *Elephas primigenius*, would not fit into such a system, since it had an elephant's flat teeth but lived in a cold climate. It was, in fact, a mammoth; and mammoths, as Jefferson did not understand, were simply one type of elephant. He overlooked the important point that the European and Siberian animals both had elephant-like teeth, and that his Big Bone Lick animals had a different sort of teeth.

The trouble was that things were not as simple as Jefferson wanted them to be. He was correct that modern elephants are creatures of warm lands and that mammoths were found in cold lands. But he failed to understand that the mammoths of Siberia (and Europe) were elephants that were able to stand the cold, while his knobby-toothed Ohio Valley "mammoth" was not a mammoth at all—that is, a cold-weather elephant—but another kind of creature entirely, standing apart both from mammoths and from modern tropical elephants.

What led Jefferson down this false trail, it seems, was partly a matter of patriotism. He was trying to defend the animal life of North America against what he regarded as a slur by one of the world's best known naturalists, the Count de Buffon of France. Buffon, the head of the Jardin du Roi, had claimed that the animals of the New World are inferior to those of the Old World in every way, being smaller, weaker, and awkwardly shaped. He offered many facts to support this claim, all of them wrong.

In the only book he ever published, *Notes on the State of Virginia*, Jefferson devoted a good deal of space to quarreling with Buffon. Jefferson wrote this book in 1781, at a dark time in his life; he had just resigned as Governor of Virginia after an unhappy term in office, his infant daughter had died, the outcome of the Revolutionary War seemed in doubt, and British troops had just invaded and set fire to Virginia's capital city, Richmond. Depressed and exhausted, Jefferson retired to the seclusion of his estate at Monticello and took his mind from his woes by compiling an essay on the history, geography, natural history, laws, and products of his native state.

In attacking Buffon's theory, Jefferson drew up long lists of animals found both in the New World and the Old, and supplied tables of measurements to show that the New World's animals are no smaller, on the average, than those of the Old World, and in many cases are a good deal bigger. Jefferson's prize example was the Ohio Valley "mammoth." Buffon accepted his assistant Daubenton's view that the Ohio Valley tusks and bones were those of an elephant and the grinders those of a hippopotamus; furthermore, Buffon said, the American elephant was nothing special in size, as elephants went. As we have seen, Jefferson rejected that view. The big, knobby teeth came from the same animal as did the tusks, and that animal, he claimed, was the mammoth. Moreover, Jefferson's "mammoth" was far mightier than any elephant, and proved the superiority of the New World. On the basis of the size of its teeth alone, Jefferson insisted, the "mammoth" of the Ohio Valley must have been five or six times as bulky as the biggest elephant!

Jefferson also battled with Buffon over the question of the mammoth's present-day whereabouts. For Buffon there was no problem, since he did not believe in Jefferson's knobby-toothed "mammoth." The knobby teeth, so far as Buffon was concerned, came from a hippopotamus whose remains had become mixed with those of elephants. To Buffon there was only a single tribe of elephants, found in Europe, Africa, Asia, North America, and perhaps other places. The fossils dug up in the Ohio Valley belonged to that tribe; so did those found in Siberia. Elephants were the same everywhere except in a few minor details.

Buffon did not have to account for any extinct species. He believed that the world had been created about 75,000 years ago, and that when it was young it was a fiery ball of liquid metal. It has been gradually growing cooler ever since, starting at the poles. Long ago, the whole world was warm enough to permit tropical animals such as elephants to exist everywhere. But as the planet cooled, the zone where these warmth-loving beasts could live grew steadily smaller, according to Buffon, and so they were gradually forced out of such places as Europe, North America, and Siberia. Today they live only near the equator, but the bones of their ancestors remain in colder lands to testify to the way the world's climate has changed.

Jefferson accepted none of this. Why is it, he wondered, that no elephants are found living in the tropical regions of South and Central America? If Buffon were right, the elephants of the Ohio Valley would have migrated there to keep warm.

More to the point, Jefferson argued, the Big Bone Lick creatures had not been elephants but rather "mammoths," different and much larger animals with distinctive teeth. In making this claim, though, Jefferson was faced with a subtle difficulty. Why had no one ever seen a living specimen of this American "mammoth" in which he took such pride? Could it be that the animal was . . . extinct?

The idea that species could become extinct went against Jefferson's philosophical convictions. He was a believer in the "great chain of being" concept, and once declared that the "intelligent and powerful Agent" that directed the universe would not permit it to be "reduced to a shapeless chaos" by the extinction of species.

Where were the American mammoths living, then?

Jefferson thought that there must still be some in the northern parts of the continent. If the animal were carnivorous, he said, it might have retreated to remote places because the spread of civilization had wiped out the game animals on which it fed.

To support this theory Jefferson collected Indian traditions concerning the existence of a giant carnivorous animal with elephant-like features. Many stories of such beasts were then told by the Indians;

most of them, probably, were inspired by the white man's own inquiries about elephants. When Europeans came asking if the Indians had seen animals with tusks and long noses, the Indians frequently were glad to supply useful answers.

So an Algonquin tribe told of a mighty animal "with an arm coming out of its shoulder"—a trunk? —and of another beast that left "large round tracks in the snow" and "struck its enemies with its long nose." A myth of the Penobscot Indians told of "moving hills without vegetation" that turned out to be, on close inspection, "great animals with long teeth, animals so huge that when they lay down they could not get up." The Chitimacha Indians of Louisiana said, "A long time ago a being with a long nose came out of the ocean and began to kill people. It would root up trees with its nose to get at people who sought refuge in the branches."

Jefferson missed no opportunity to acquire such stories. In 1780, while he was Governor of Virginia, a delegation of Lenni Lenape Indians who lived near Big Bone Lick came to see him on matters of tribal business. After the meeting Jefferson asked them what they could tell him about the animal whose bones were found there, and the chief replied:

In ancient times a herd of these tremendous animals came to the Big Bone Lick, and began a universal destruction of the bear, deer, elks, buffaloes, and other animals, which had been created for the use of the Indians. The Great Man above, look-

ing down and seeing this, was so enraged
that he seized his lightning, descended on
the earth, seated himself on a neighboring
mountain, on a rock, on which his seat and
the print of his feet are still to be seen,
and hurled his bolts among them till the
whole were slaughtered, except the big
bull, who presenting his forehead to the
shafts, shook them off as they fell; but
missing one at length, it wounded him in
the side; whereon, springing round, he
bounded over the Ohio, over the Wabash,
the Illinois, and finally over the Great
Lakes, where he is living at this day.

Despite such reports, American explorers failed
to find mammoths anywhere as they cautiously
moved westward in the 1780's. Jefferson did not
give up hope. In 1785, when he became the United
States Ambassador to France, Jefferson sought out
Buffon and continued the argument face to face, insisting that the Ohio Valley "mammoth" was an animal quite different from the Old World elephant,
that it was much larger than any elephant, and that
it must still exist somewhere in western North America. Buffon, a suave and elegant individual, did not
attempt to argue with Jefferson. He merely took
down a copy of his latest book, gave it to the American, and said, "When Mr. Jefferson shall have read
this, he will be perfectly satisfied that I am right."

Buffon could not convince Jefferson of anything,
nor could Jefferson convince Buffon. For the next
decade, no one in Europe or the United States seems

to have offered any useful new ideas about the giant fossil bones. Then, in 1797, the American Philosophical Society of Philadelphia heard a paper by George Turner—a judge whose hobby was natural history —in which several of Jefferson's errors were corrected.

Turner saw, as the brilliant Jefferson did not, that the elephant-like fossils being discovered in the United States were actually of two kinds. One was the Big Bone Lick animal with the knobby teeth, which Jefferson insisted on calling a "mammoth." The other was an animal with flat, ridged grinders; this beast was very similar to the fossil elephants of Europe and the living elephants of Africa and Asia. Both of these creatures—the "mammoth" and the elephant—had evidently ranged the United States in bygone years. Both must now be extinct in North America, Turner said, for it seemed impossible to him "that so many and such stupendous creatures could exist for centuries and be concealed from the prying eye of inquisitive man."

The American elephant, Turner rightly said, had had a diet of plants. But like so many others Turner was fooled by the fierce-looking teeth of the Ohio Valley "mammoth," and decided that that animal must have been carnivorous. "With the agility and ferocity of the tiger, with a body of unequalled magnitude and strength, it is possible that the mammoth may have been at once the terror of the forest and of man!" Turner wrote.

The story of the fossil elephants still needed some further disentangling. In 1799, an extraordinary

French scientist named Georges Cuvier began to investigate the tangled situation as part of a general study he was making of all extinct animals.

The word "extinct" held no philosophical or religious terrors for Cuvier. It was obvious to him that many forms of life had disappeared since the world began. These extinctions came about, he believed, through catastrophes. Great floods or other natural upheavals had again and again wiped clean the slate of life. Noah's Deluge was only the most recent of these catastrophes. After each disaster, God had created new forms of life. Cuvier did not attempt to say exactly how many catastrophes there had been since the beginning of life on Earth, but one of his disciples, d'Orbigny, worked out an intricate scheme of twenty-seven successive acts of creation and destruction.

Cuvier's theory of catastrophes won wide acceptance in its day. It was in many ways a comforting notion, for it allowed people to reconcile the evidence of the fossils with the teachings of the Bible. Those who had felt all along that mammoths and other odd creatures were "antediluvian" beings now had the prestige of a great scientist like Cuvier on their side.

One of Cuvier's gifts was a deep understanding of anatomy and skeletal structure, for which he had been nicknamed "the Pope of Bones." He applied this gift in settling the vexed question of the elephants and the elephant-like fossils, and by 1806 he had everything sorted out properly.

Living elephants, Cuvier confirmed, are of two

distinct types, so different from one another that they should not even be classed in the same species. Under the system of classification that had been invented by the eighteenth-century Swedish naturalist Carolus Linnaeus, all living things were given Latin names according to their *genus* and their *species*. The genus (plural, *genera*) is the broad family grouping, the species a particular section within that family. Thus we have a genus of dogs, *Canis*, which includes such species as *Canis lupus* (the European gray wolf), *Canis occidentalis* (the American timber wolf), *Canis latrans* (the coyote), and *Canis familiaris* (the domestic dog). The various breeds of domestic dog—spaniel, dachshund, poodle, and so on—are regarded as breeds, or races, within the species *Canis familiaris*.

The first attempts to classify the elephants saw both the African and Asian kinds put in the same genus, *Elephas*. Cuvier corrected this, showing that the differences in number of ribs, hooves, and vertebrae, shape of trunk and ears, length of tusks, and so on, made it necessary to put these two similar-looking animals in separate genera. He took the African elephant out of the genus *Elephas* and coined a new generic name, *Loxodonta,* for it. (It means "slant-tooth," and describes the shape taken by the ridges on the African elephant's grinders as they wear down.) Most zoologists today still accept this classification, calling the Asian elephant *Elephas maximus* and the African elephant *Loxodonta africana.*

Then Cuvier turned to the fossils. He said that all

the elephant-like animals found in fossil form were extinct, and that all, regardless of the shape of their grinding teeth, had been plant-eaters. Thus two myths were swept away.

Johann Blumenbach, in 1799, had shown that the European fossil elephant was similar to modern elephants, but belonged in a species of its own. He named it *Elephas primigenius*. When Adams obtained a complete mammoth skeleton in Siberia in 1806, Blumenbach declared that the Siberian animal and the fossils from Europe were identical. Cuvier accepted this line of thought. He, too, classed the mammoths— both European and Siberian—as *Elephas primigenius*. Some of the fossils found in the New World also were mammoth remains, Cuvier said, and belonged in this species.

However, most of the elephant-like fossils that had been unearthed thus far in North America did not belong to the genus *Elephas* at all. Their knob-studded teeth marked them as members of a separate genus. These were the animals which Jefferson and George Turner had called "mammoths," but Cuvier insisted that that name could not be used for them, since it properly should be applied to the Siberian fossil elephant, and the Ohio Valley animal did not have an elephant's teeth. Cuvier suggested calling the Ohio Valley animal a "mastodon," meaning "breast-tooth," in view of the breast-shaped bulges on their grinding surfaces.

The new name helped to clear up some of the confusion. What Jefferson thought of as a "mammoth" was really a mastodon. True mammoths had also existed in the New World as well as in Europe and Siberia, but they were elephants.

Giving the mastodon a formal Latin name turned out to be a complicated chore, though. In 1792, the zoologist Robert Kerr had named it *Elephas americanus*. Clearly this name would not do, since the mastodon did not belong in the genus *Elephas* at all. Seven years later another name was proposed, apparently in ignorance of the one Kerr had bestowed. The new name, *Mammut americanum*, was even worse, since it specifically identified the Ohio Valley animal as a mammoth. Then Cuvier coined the word "mastodon," and in 1814 the naturalist Constantine Rafinesque suggested that the Big Bone Lick animal be classified as *Mastodon americanus*. Most scientists today use that name, although a few textbooks of zoology insist on calling the mastodon by the confusing name of *Mammut americanum,* simply because that name won general backing before Rafinesque's was put forth.

In any case, the behemoth of the New World now had a scientific name—several of them, in fact.

"MAMMOTH FEVER"

CHAPTER FOUR

The first half of the nineteenth century was marked by tremendous public interest in mammoths and mastodons on both sides of the Atlantic. The idea that great herds of elephants had roamed Europe and America in prehistoric days held a powerful fascination. Every new discovery of a fossil skeleton was greeted with excitement; every surprising new theory about these mighty animals and the era in which they had lived became the subject of heated debate.

In the United States, Thomas Jefferson was at the center of most of the activity involving the "mammoth," as he would call the mastodon to the end of his life. Jefferson was elected Vice President of the United States in 1796, but the duties of that post were even more trifling then than they are today, and he was left with plenty of time to pursue his scientific interests. In 1797, therefore, he took on the additional position of president of the American Philosophical Society, the young nation's leading scientific organization.

At the first meeting of the society over which Jefferson presided, on May 19, 1797, he proposed "A Plan for Collecting Information Respecting the Antiquities of North America." In particular he hoped to collect the complete skeleton of a "mammoth," since only tusks, teeth, and scattered bones of this animal had thus far been found. The American Philosophical Society picked a seven-man committee to consider Jefferson's plan. Among its members were Jefferson, George Turner, and two distinguished Philadelphians, the physician-naturalist Caspar Wistar and the artist-naturalist Charles Willson Peale. At the end of 1798 this committee sent circulars throughout the country, seeking help in obtaining "one or more entire skeletons of the Mammoth, so called, and of such other unknown animals as either have been, or hereafter may be discovered in America."

Despite the best efforts of the committee, no news of "mammoth" skeletons was heard in 1799 or in 1800. However, in 1801, Charles Willson Peale read a newspaper article telling of the discovery two years earlier of giant bones on the farm of John Masten in Orange County, New York. Peale set out quickly for Masten's farm to see if any of the bones still existed.

Peale had a double reason for his interest in the Masten fossils. As an officer of the American Philosophical Society, he naturally wanted to rescue these possibly important relics for science. But Peale also ran a museum in Philadelphia, and he knew that the skeleton of a "mammoth" would make an exciting exhibit.

Peale's museum was the first museum of natural history in America. It had begun shortly after the American Revolution simply as a private collection of curiosities in Peale's own house; its early treasures included some mastodon bones from Big Bone Lick, a few stuffed animals, and an Angora cat sent from France as a gift from Benjamin Franklin. While winning a reputation for himself as a painter of portraits— he was best known for his many portrayals of George Washington—Peale continued to collect things, and in 1785 opened his collection to the public by selling admission tickets. Nine years later, in need of more room to house his growing museum, Peale rented a large room in the building of the American Philosophical Society. Jefferson served for a time as president of the museum's board of directors.

Peale was a clever showman as well as a tireless collector; though his museum's main interest was natural history, he brought the public into it with such additional attractions as musical recitals, paintings of famous men, and "magic" mirrors of the kind seen at amusement parks. But its great value was its scientific displays—1,100 different kinds of birds, 3,450 insects, 250 mammals, as well as minerals, fishes, shells, coins, clothing from exotic lands, and other curios. The animals were cunningly mounted in lifelike poses with painted backgrounds to show their usual habitats.

When Peale arrived at John Masten's farm he found the bones—which were those of a mastodon—in poor shape. Upon their discovery in 1799, Masten and about one hundred of his neighbors had spent two days energetically uncovering the relics. Unfortunately, some liquor was passed around during the work and many of the men became "impatient and unruly," in Peale's words, smashing a number of the bones in their tipsy carelessness. Also, some of the heaviest bones had been dragged from the ground with an ox and chains, and as a result the skull, tusks, and hipbones were badly damaged.

The bones that remained were in Masten's barn, where he had them on exhibit for a small fee. Battered as they were, they were the closest thing to a complete mastodon skeleton that had ever been found, and Peale offered Masten $200 for the bones and $100 more for the right to dig on his land for other fossils. Masten accepted, after getting Peale to agree to throw in a rifle for his son and gowns for his daughters. Peale took the bones back with him to Philadelphia.

On July 24, 1801, Peale sent a report on his trip to his friend Jefferson, who then was living in the White House, having been elected President of the United States in 1800. Peale said he believed that more "mammoth" bones could be found in the pit where Masten had discovered the first ones, but unhappily the pit had filled with water. Was it possible for Jefferson to lend him one of the government's pumps to empty it? Jefferson answered four days later that "the Secretary of the Navy will give orders immediately to the Navy agent at New York to lend you a pump." Jefferson also instructed the Army's commanding officer at Philadelphia to provide Peale with some tents. This seems to have been the first time that the government of the United States had offered aid to a scientific expedition. The government could not lend Peale money, though, and he borrowed $500 from the American Philosophical Society to finance the costs of his excavations.

Amid much local excitement, Peale began work. His son Rembrandt Peale, writing in 1803, tells how "rich and poor, men, women, and children, all flocked to see the operation." The Navy's pump was not suitable, and to drain the pit Peale had to rig buckets on a chain, which he fastened to a huge framework of logs from which it could dangle into the hole. The chain was connected to a wooden wheel 20 feet in diameter, mounted upright and wide enough for two or three men to walk in it "as squirrels in a cage," Peale said. This human-powered wheel turned the bucket-chain, so that each bucket in turn dipped into the pit, scooped up water, and emptied its load into a nearby trough. The elaborate device was able to remove more than 1400 gallons of water an hour, and with it Peale succeeded in keeping the pit empty even though fast-flowing springs constantly poured new water into it.

Out of the mud at the bottom came a broken tusk,

parts of the skull, all the ribs, and a number of minor bones. The lower jaw and some other important parts were missing, though, and after Peale concluded he would not find them on Masten's farm, he did some digging at nearby sites where fossils had also been found. One farm eleven miles away yielded tusks, ribs, and bones of the feet and tail, but no lower jaw. Peale moved on to a third farm, where more ribs and foot bones turned up, and then, after a long and disappointing spell without discoveries, a perfect lower jaw, complete except for one grinder.

Back in Philadelphia, Peale combined his assortment of mastodon bones into two assembled skeletons, one nearly complete, the other missing a number of bones. His son Rembrandt filled in the deficiencies of the better skeleton by carving replicas of some tail bones and a piece of the skull out of wood. In April, 1803, Peale notified Jefferson that the "mammoth" skeleton was finished and had gone on display in his museum. Its length from the tusks to the tip of the tail was 30 feet 6 inches; it was 11 feet 10 inches high at the shoulders, 9 feet 1 inch high at the hips.

Philadelphians came out in great numbers to view this wonder, the first fossil skeleton ever mounted in America. Oddly, it proved disappointing to some. Mrs. Anne Royall, who wrote a brief account of her visit to Peale's museum, declared, "The skeleton is indeed as large as is represented, but it had not that formidable, dread-inspiring aspect which my romantic turn led me to expect, and with which I expected to be overwhelmed: I beheld it without surprise or emotion.'' Two gentlemen who were there the same day were not only unimpressed but skeptical; one of them, slipping under the rail to have a close look, scraped one of the huge bones with his penknife and, Mrs. Royall wrote, ''swore 'it was nothing but wood.' ''

In reality Peale's mastodon was a majestic sight that should have overpowered all viewers. It was disappointing only because some writers had published fantastic speculations on how big the ''mammoth'' must have been. One such estimate spoke of an animal 133 feet long and 105 feet high. Jefferson himself apparently thought that the ''mammoth'' might be 50 to 100 feet long and 40 to 80 feet high. Now, for the first time, a complete skeleton of the ''mammoth'' was on show, and it was merely as large as a large elephant. After the tremendous buildup, the reality was no match for the monster of the imagination.

Even so, the United States had an epidemic of ''mammoth'' fever. The word ''mammoth'' itself acquired a new meaning, becoming an adjective used to describe anything of great size. A Philadelphia baker offered ''mammoth bread''—oversized loaves. A man in Washington proclaimed himself a ''mammoth eater'' and downed forty-two eggs in ten minutes to prove it. Some of Jefferson's admirers in Massachusetts produced a ''mammoth cheese'' weighing 1,235 pounds, and delivered it to him in Washington aboard a wagon drawn by four horses. Jefferson put it on exhibit in the East Room of the

White House, which he nicknamed "the Mammoth Room." Jefferson's political enemies made his interest in mammoths a feature of their attacks on him, calling him "a mammoth infidel" and similar names.

Delighted as he was with Peale's "mammoth," Jefferson still was eager to see new specimens discovered. In 1803, upon learning that a Cincinnati physician named William Goforth had recently conducted some excavations at Big Bone Lick, Jefferson sent his private secretary, Meriwether Lewis, to question Dr. Goforth about his finds.

Lewis was then on his way west anyway. Jefferson had just doubled the size of the United States by purchasing the vast territory known as Louisiana from France—more than 800,000 square miles of wilderness west of the Mississippi—and he had chosen Lewis, along with William Clark of Virginia, to explore this immense domain. Lewis and Clark were instructed to meet at St. Louis, gather supplies and men, and set forth toward the Pacific; along the way they were supposed to study the geography, natural history, Indian life, climate, minerals, and commercial possibilities of the newly acquired territory.

Late in September, 1803, Lewis arrived in Cincinnati, which is about twenty miles from Big Bone Lick. He sought out Dr. Goforth, and learned that the physician had dug at the fossil site four months before, sinking a pit 30 feet square and 11 feet deep in a moist part of the area. His hope had been to find a complete skeleton of the "mammoth" to place on exhibition as a moneymaking venture. Goforth had succeeded in collecting a great many bones and tusks of "mammoths"—actually these were mastodon remains—and also had found several flat grinders of the elephant type. These were the teeth of the true mammoth, but since Americans were still using the word "mammoth" for the mastodon, Goforth simply called them elephant teeth. He gave Lewis a ten-pound elephant grinder and also a mastodon tooth, along with a large tusk and some other fossil specimens. Lewis shipped them down the Mississippi so they could be forwarded to President Jefferson, but the boat carrying them sank at Natchez and the fossils went to the bottom of the river.

Lewis continued westward for his rendezvous with Clark at St. Louis. The explorers began their great adventure in the spring of 1804. Jefferson had instructed them to search for live mammoths west of the Mississippi, insisting that "in the present interior of our continent there is surely space enough" for such creatures; but when Lewis and Clark returned to civilization late in 1806 they were forced to report that they had not seen a single mammoth alive anywhere, though they had come upon a few fossil bones.

Then Jefferson asked Clark to collect bones for him at Big Bone Lick. Clark went there in the summer of 1807, hiring ten laborers with money Jefferson supplied, and excavated about three hundred bones. They included specimens both of the mastodon and the true mammoth, and also fossils of extinct species of bison, deer, and oxen. Again the relics were shipped down the Mississippi, and this time they arrived safely in New Orleans to be forwarded back up the coast to Washington. Early in 1808 they reached the White House; Jefferson installed them in the East Room, which some years earlier had housed his "mammoth cheese."

He asked Dr. Caspar Wistar, the noted anatomist and naturalist from Philadelphia, to examine the collection. Jefferson intended to keep one "mammoth" tusk and a thighbone as ornaments for his home at Monticello, since he would be leaving the Presidency the following year; but he told Wistar to select from the other items anything that he thought the American Philosophical Society might want to have. "The bones are spread in a large room," Jefferson told Wistar, "where you can work at your leisure, undisturbed by any mortal, from morning till night, taking your breakfast and dinner with us."

Wistar patiently sorted bones in the White House for several weeks. He chose for the Society a number of the smaller bones of the mastodon, since by now the large ones were becoming quite common. Afterward, Jefferson sent the remaining fossils to the National Institute of France, along with a letter explaining that he was making the gift because it was his recollection that the collection of bones of the Ohio animal "sometimes called Mammoth" in the possession of the French natural history museum "is not very copious." Jefferson's recollection was correct; the only specimens of this animal the French had were the few items brought back by Longueuil seventy years before. The grateful scientists of France sent Jefferson a formal letter of thanks.

But Cuvier, ''the Pope of Bones,'' examined the fossils and saw at once that they were the remains of mastodons, not of mammoths. Apparently he did not try to correct the error that Jefferson so persistently made.

MAMMOTHS, MEN, AND ICE

European scientists had managed to grasp the difference between mammoths and mastodons, but they were still puzzled by a far more difficult question: how elephants had been able to tolerate the cold winters of Europe and the incredibly colder winters of Siberia. Two suggestions presented themselves, both disturbing ones. Either the world had once been much warmer, or else the mammoth had been a variety of elephant that could stand great cold.

These ideas were troublesome because they implied the possibility that the world or the creatures in it could undergo major changes. At the beginning of the nineteenth century most laymen, and most scientists as well, still accepted the belief that the world had been created by God in six days, and that nothing—neither the climate nor the species of animals and plants—had altered since Adam and Eve dwelled in the Garden of Eden. The discovery of the fossilized remains of unknown creatures had helped to sway this belief; but, as we have seen, such theories as Cuvier's notion of catastrophes kept the Biblical teachings alive.

All sorts of evidence kept coming to light that challenged the old beliefs, however. As scientists examined new fossil discoveries, and compared information gathered in one region with information gathered in another, certain patterns of truth began to emerge. A few bold men were able to recognize that both climate and species *can* change over long periods of time.

When Mikhail Adams saw Ossip Shumakov's thawed-out mammoth carcass in 1806, the secret of how elephants could have stood Siberian cold became apparent. The mammoth had been wrapped in a dense fur coat, a thick blanket of woolly hair offering protection against the worst of climates. Nor was it the only supposedly "tropical" creature that had found a way of adapting to severe cold. In 1771 the German explorer Peter Simon Pallas, wandering through Siberia, had come across the thawed-out carcass of a rhinoceros which also had had a thick woolly coat. Elephants and rhinoceroses are practically hairless in the tropics; but by the early nineteenth century it was clear that once there had been species of these animals capable of sprouting fur and living in the north.

Why did such species no longer exist?

Winter scene

Cuvier had the answer, and it was an old answer in a new guise: the theory of catastrophes. Mammoths were antediluvian, he said. They had lived prior to some tremendous world-wide catastrophe that had killed all life. Cuvier's theory was simply the tale of Noah and his Ark, without Noah.

After the catastrophe, God had created new animals, according to Cuvier. Some of these animals resembled those that had lived in the former age, but they were not necessarily identical. Before the catastrophe, God had chosen to create hairy elephants and rhinoceroses that could withstand the cold. But in the new creation, He had brought into being different species of elephants and rhinoceroses that were naked and had to live in the tropics. No one could say why. It was not given to man to understand the Creator's motives.

What about man himself? What was his place in Cuvier's theory?

Here Cuvier departed completely from the Biblical version. The Bible declared that man also had been antediluvian, and had survived the Deluge only because Noah and his family had lived to carry on the human race. Cuvier said that man had been created after the Deluge. He was a product of very recent times. "There is no such thing as fossil man," Cuvier insisted.

It seemed quite logical and understandable. But then people began to make awkward discoveries—discoveries proving that man had lived at the same time as the extinct antediluvian beasts, that man himself was an antediluvian being!

Actually such discoveries had been made long before Cuvier's time. The pharmacist named Conyers who dug up elephant bones in London in 1715 and found a stone ax lying with them had uncovered a weapon of a prehistoric mammoth-hunter. Conyers had no way of knowing that, so he said the elephant had come to Britain with the Romans and the ax had belonged to a native British warrior. About sixty years later, a German priest named Johann Friedrich Esper, digging for fossils in a cave, unearthed the bones of a huge bear of a type no longer seen anywhere. Esper concluded that the bear must have been an antediluvian creature, a victim of the Deluge. He kept digging and found a human jawbone in the same level of the earth.

In 1790, an English gentleman named John Frere, doing some archaeological excavation twelve feet below the surface of the ground, discovered several stone axes made of chipped flint. Lying near them, he said, were "some extraordinary bones, particularly a jawbone of enormous size, of some unknown animal, with the teeth remaining in it." Frere suggested, "The situation in which these weapons were found may tempt us to refer them to a very remote period indeed; even beyond that of the present world."

Those discoveries all had been made before Cuvier proclaimed, in his theory of catastrophes, that there had been no antediluvian humans. He simply brushed them aside as unimportant or mistaken. That was what he did in 1820 when Baron Ernst Friedrich von Schlotheim, a German paleontologist, unearthed human teeth among some mammoth remains at the town of Köstritz. Did that mean that men and mammoths had been contemporaries there? No, said Cuvier. Some gravedigger of Köstritz must have dug unusually deep, so that a citizen of the town went to his eternal rest buried down in ancient levels of the earth dating from antediluvian times.

But the discoveries continued. In 1824, a Roman Catholic priest, Father MacEnery, found flint tools and the bones of the extinct woolly rhinoceros in Kent's Cavern, Devon, England. An unbroken layer of stalagmite covered the relics, which seemed to prove that they were all of the same age. The priest reported his find to William Buckland, an English theologian and an expert on fossils. Buckland argued that the flint tools had somehow slipped down through the stalagmite layer into the lower, older layer of extinct animals. There were no antediluvian men, Buckland pointed out.

In 1828, a French museum curator named Tournal found human bones and those of extinct animals mixed together in a grotto near Narbone. Some of the animal bones showed signs that they had been carved by human tools. In Belgium, a doctor named Schmerling found seven human skulls, many flint tools, and the bones of extinct creatures such as the mammoth and the woolly rhinoceros in caves about 1830; the human bones were in precisely the same condition as those of the ancient animals. "There can be no doubt," Dr. Schmerling announced, "that the human bones were buried at the same time and by the same cause as the other extinct species."

The evidence mounted. There was ample proof now that man had lived at that time in the unknown past when Europe had been the home of hairy elephants and rhinoceroses. Even Cuvier, before his death in 1832, hesitantly admitted the possibility that man just might have lived before the last upheaval of the globe. "He might have inhabited certain circumscribed regions," Cuvier wrote, "whence he repeopled the earth after these terrible events; perhaps even the places he inhabited were entirely swallowed up and his bones buried in the depths of the present seas, except for a small number of individuals who carried on the race." The story of Noah might be a poetic rendering of such an occurrence.

Another blow to the catastrophe theory was struck by a geologist, Charles Lyell. In his great book *Principles of Geology,* published in three volumes between 1830 and 1833, Lyell declared that the forces of nature had operated more or less uniformly throughout time; perhaps there had been great floods and other catastrophes, but they had not been the prime changer of the world's surface or of its living things. Lyell had examined the geological evidence: mountain streams cutting ever deeper gorges through rock, rivers hauling tons of silt to the ocean, wind and rain changing the face of the land. He saw that these were processes that worked infinitely slowly; they must have been going on for millions of years. Mountains rose, erosion cut them down—but there could not have been the violent upheavals on which Cuvier's theory was based.

The fossil record bolstered Lyell's views. It could

now be seen that many creatures—certain crabs and snails, and even the common cockroach—had survived practically unchanged over incredible spans of time. Their remains were found in the oldest rocks, those deep in the ground. Why had these creatures not been destroyed by the repeated catastrophes? Had God re-created them after each deluge, each volcanic outpouring? There had not been four or eight or twenty-seven separate acts of creation, as Cuvier and his disciples thought. Certain species had vanished from the world over the years—and no one could say why—but others had remained, century after century, millennium after millennium.

Even after the catastrophe theory began to fade, though, Cuvier's ideas about the nonexistence of antediluvian man lingered on among many influential scientists. They would not believe that man and mammoth had been contemporaries—even when they were shown the points of the weapons with which man had hunted the great hairy elephants, and the stone knives with which he had sliced up their meat.

A French customs official named Jacques Boucher de Crèvecoeur de Perthes devoted much of his life to finding those weapons and tools. Beginning in 1825, Boucher de Perthes, as he was usually known, began to search for fossils near the town of Abbeville in northern France. While examining a gravel pit just outside of town, he came upon pieces of flint that appeared to have been chipped by human hands into a useful shape. Possibly the shape of these flints was the result of accidental breakage, and looked like human work only through coincidence. But in 1832 he found a stone ax that was unmistakably man-made, for it was rounded at one end to fit the hand, chipped to a point at the other. His excitement rising, Boucher de Perthes continued to explore the gravel beds near Abbeville. He turned up more axes, as well as knives, awls, weapon points, and scrapers, all of stone. With these artifacts were the bones of mammoths, rhinoceroses, bison, cave lions, and other extinct beasts of the "antediluvian" era.

When he claimed to have found human tools and weapons with these animal bones, other French experts on prehistory laughed at him. When he published a five-volume book describing his finds, they ignored it. "They did not discuss my facts, they did not even take the trouble to deny them," Boucher de Perthes lamented. "They disregarded them." He persisted, though, and some of those who scorned him took a closer look at his work, or conducted excavations of their own, and were converted. A discovery made in England in 1858 lent support to Boucher de Perthes' claims: a schoolmaster named William Pengelly excavated a cave in Devon on whose floor lay a sheet of stalagmite three to eight inches thick. On and within this sheet were the bones of mammoth, rhinoceros, reindeer, lion, hyena, and bear. Below it—sealed by thousands of years of stalagmite formation—Pengelly found flint tools.

Only a few diehards clung to the old beliefs now —such as Élie de Beaumont, head of the French Academy of Sciences, who said in 1863, "I do not think the human species was contemporary with *Ele-*

phas primigenius. Cuvier's opinion was the work of a genius. It has not been overthrown.''

A year later, two archaeologists working in southwest France produced the best possible proof that man had lived at the same time as the mammoth: a flat piece of ivory on which some gifted prehistoric artist had carved a superb drawing of a mammoth! It looked like an elephant, yes, with a long trunk and great curving tusks and a massive head. But it was covered with shaggy hair, and it had a strange hump on its head, evidently a mass of fat, which no one could have known about simply by examining a mammoth's fossil skull. (Nor had the head of Ossip Shumakhov's thawed-out mammoth been well enough preserved to show such a feature.)

The discoverers of this astonishing masterpiece of prehistoric art were Edouard Lartet, a French lawyer, and Henry Christy, a British banker. Both had lost interest in their professions and had surrendered completely to the fascination of uncovering the secrets of the past. Lartet had long been convinced of the truth of Boucher de Perthes' ideas about men and mammoths, and in 1859 had made an important discovery of his own at a cave near the village of Aurignac, in the Pyrenees. The upper level of the cave contained elegant stone tools that had been carefully rubbed and polished into shape. Below them—and therefore older—lay an assortment of crude chipped flint tools, implements of bone and ivory, and the fossilized bones of extinct animals such as the mammoth and the woolly rhinoceros. No such bones could be found with the more recent polished-stone tools. Evidently the shaggy beasts had vanished from this part of Europe at a time when man still was living in the stone age, but before he had learned to shape his tools by polishing instead of by chipping away flakes of stone.

In 1863 Lartet and his friend Christy began to explore the rock shelters of the Dordogne district of southwest France, where amateur archaeologists had noticed a great many prehistoric stone tools. A rock shelter is not a true cave, but simply an overhanging ledge with a huddling-place beneath. Early man had camped in many of the rock shelters of the Dordogne, leaving behind discarded tools and the bones of slaughtered animals.

At one such site, Laugerie Haute, the accumulation of ancient human debris was fourteen feet thick. Cutting down through this heap of bones, shells, flints, ashes, charcoal, and other refuse, Lartet and Christy were able to follow the changes in human culture over a period of thousands of years. The topmost layer yielded finely worked stone blades. Bones of reindeer and wild horses were associated with these flints. Below, and therefore older, was a layer of less elegant stone tools, mixed with the fossils of mammoth and rhinoceros bones. Even cruder tools lay beneath. At the nearby rock shelter of La Madeleine they were able to find another sequence of tools, the most recent matching the oldest type of Laugerie Haute. Eventually Lartet and Christy had put together a sequence of seven types of stone tools, ranging from early, extremely crude stone axes to delicate and graceful work from the highest layers.

In the upper levels Lartet and Christy discovered

the first traces of prehistoric art: pieces of bone and ivory on which the images of animals had been carved. They saw recognizable horses, reindeer, bison—and then, at La Madeleine, the ponderous and shaggy form of a mammoth. It was easy for skeptics to dismiss it as a fake; but those who knew the reputations of Lartet and Christy realized it must be genuine, unmistakable proof that men and mammoths had shared this French valley long ago.

Another important and surprising discovery came from the lower levels of the rock shelters, below the layers where mammoth and rhinoceros bones were found. Associated with the crudest tools of all were elephant and rhinoceros fossils of a different sort— bones more like those of the tropical species in existence today than like those of the woolly cold-weather species. Comparison of other animal species found in the different layers gradually revealed a similar pattern. For a while, it seemed, Europe had been inhabited by animals best suited to the tropics. Then had come a group of animals adapted to weather as cold as Siberia's. Lastly, these woolly beasts had disappeared and animals more like those of modern Europe had developed.

From the fossil evidence in the rock shelters Lartet divided the ancient history of Europe into three epochs. First had come a Hippopotamus Age, when Europe was warm and tropical, inhabited by beasts similar to those now found in Africa. Then came a time of cold which he called the Mammoth Age, when ice descended on Europe and men took shelter in caves. Lastly came the Reindeer Age, when the

Primitive outline engravings of mammoths from walls
of Caverns of Combarelles and Font-de-Gaume

weather began to relent, and man started to learn the skills of civilization.

We know now that Lartet's system was much too simple. But his basic idea, that of a succession of warm and cold eras, is still accepted. Again and again Europe was subjected to ice ages, and it was in several of those harsh periods that the woolly mammoth flourished.

Geologists had been discussing theories of ice ages since the early nineteenth century. They had noticed that boulders and rocky rubble were scattered over much of Europe, as though strewn by a giant's hand. Some of this debris lay just north of the Alps, and Swiss scientists pointed out that it could have been carried there by glaciers in a time of great cold, when these rivers of ice reached far beyond their present limits. The bedrock of the regions where the debris was found was scraped, polished, and grooved—a good indication that glaciers had passed that way.

But glacial debris of this kind could be observed far from the Alps—in northern Germany, in Scandinavia, in the British Isles, where no one had ever seen an alpine glacier. At first it was explained by saying that the waters of Noah's Deluge had carried this material across the continent. But that did not account for the scraped and grooved bedrock, which could have been produced only by the grinding of some unimaginably heavy force over the face of the land. A few bold scientists suggested that Europe might once have been covered by a colossal glacial ice sheet, extending from the North Pole to the Alps.

The Swiss zoologist Louis Agassiz was the most vigorous backer of this theory. In 1840 he published a book called *Glacial Studies,* based on research in the debris areas of Europe, which argued that "great sheets of ice, resembling those now existing in Greenland, once covered all the countries in which unstratified gravel [boulder drift] is found." Later Agassiz moved to the United States and demonstrated that North America, too, had had its ice age.

Glacial debris, polished rock, and deposits of the remains of cold-weather plants and animals proved beyond any doubt that the world had experienced drastic and prolonged temperature drops. At many sites, an alternation of glacial and warm-weather deposits could be observed. By the early twentieth century it was clear that in the past million years there had been a series of glaciations interrupted by lengthy periods of mild weather. Most scientists today accept a sequence of four major ice ages, each lasting from 50,000 to 240,000 years. The fourth ice age is thought to have come to an end about 10,000 years ago.

The onset of each ice age was gradual. For some reason (we do not know why, though there are dozens of theories) temperatures began to drop by a fraction of a degree a year. Each year, the winter was a little more harsh than the previous winter; each summer was a trifle cooler. Over hundreds and thousands of years this swing in balance continued until winters were long and terrible and summers were brief. The snow that piled up in winter could not all be melted during the short summer; some of it remained, accumulating from year to year, until eventually glaciers began to flow down from the mountains onto the land.

In Europe the main ice sheet spread out of Scandinavia and reached south as far as the latitude of Berlin. In the east, another glacier covered Siberia; in the west, a smaller one engulfed the British Isles. The huge Scandinavian glacier at its greatest extent was a dazzling white blanket more than 10,000 feet thick, covering two million square miles. In southern Europe other systems of glaciers spilled down from the Pyrenees, the Apennines, the Carpathians, and the Alps. In North America all of Canada lay under ice, and the United States was covered as far south as the valleys of the Ohio and Missouri rivers. Only the highest mountain peaks stood out above the plateaus of ice, more than a mile thick, that transformed the temperate zone into a wasteland as bleak as the poles.

These shifts of climate, gradual as they were, had catastrophic effects on the plants and animals of Europe. Before the first ice age, more than a million years ago, Europe was a place of lush jungles, a land of elephant, tiger, and hippopotamus. When the weather cooled, the jungle animals began a slow retreat to the warmth of Africa and the Near East, and cold-adapted animals from the north took their place: the mammoth, the woolly rhinoceros, the musk ox, the reindeer, and other well-insulated beasts. These animals had lived along the rim of the Arctic, in the bleak tundra that was their favorite kind of country. As glaciers made northern Europe uninhabitable even for typical cold-weather animals, the mammoth and the rest moved into France and Italy and other areas that lay beyond the glacier zone.

Then the world turned warm again. Each year's summer was milder than that of the year before, and the ice boundary began to creep northward. The woolly animals started to find southern Europe growing too balmy for them, and they began a slow migration toward the north, following the glacier line as it retreated. The tropical types of animals returned to a Europe liberated from the ice.

Among the creatures that entered Europe during the mild interlude between the first and second ice ages was man. No fossil evidence has yet been discovered to show that there were human beings in Europe before the first ice age; the only human fossils found so far from that period were discovered in Africa. But on the basis of one jawbone and a good many crude tools, we know that there were humans in Europe in the tropical period after the first ice age. When the ice descended once more, perhaps half a million years ago, some of these early humans followed the elephant and the hippopotamus south, but others remained to endure the ice-age conditions.

The second ice age ended between 300,000 and 400,000 years ago, and there was another change in animal population. Once more the mammoths departed for the north and their practically hairless tropical cousins came to roam the newly reborn forests of Europe. But between 230,000 and 300,000 years ago, the glaciers advanced for the third time. Again, humans stayed to face the worsening climate, living in the Mediterranean region where the glaciers did not reach. They wrapped themselves in furry hides to keep warm, and mastered fire to some extent. The bones of the mammoth, musk ox, reindeer, and other Arctic animals are found in their sites.

It grew warm again some 170,000 to 200,000 years ago, creating another migration of beasts. Man's cultural level rose steadily, as shown by the increasing number of types of stone tools found in the sites he left, and by the improved workmanship of those tools. We know a great deal about the people who dominated Europe in the period after the third ice age. They were the Neanderthal people, who were so different in appearance from modern men that many anthropologists class them in a separate species. The Neanderthals were short and squat, with deep chests and flat feet. Their foreheads sloped backward, they had immense ridges of bone over their eyes, and their chins were rounded. They had broad, low-bridged noses and their mouths jutted forward like muzzles.

Neanderthal man was inventive, intelligent, and sturdy. He seems to have had some sort of religion; he cared for his sick and even practiced a kind of rough surgery; he buried his dead with some show of respect for their spirits. He first spread through Europe in a time of warmth, but when the fourth and (so far) last ice age got under way about 100,-000 years ago, the Neanderthals adapted to the deep freeze and remained.

The climate was again severe, but not impossible to endure, even for primitive man. In the glacier-covered north a cruel Arctic climate prevailed; even in July the temperatures rarely rose above freezing. That was true also in the glaciated mountain region running across lower Europe from the Pyrenees through the Alps and Apennines to the Carpathians. But an ice-free corridor ran across France, Germany, and eastern Europe between the Scandinavian glacier in the north and the Alpine glacier system in the south. This corridor was a tundra—a grim treeless zone where the ground was more or less permanently frozen, but where there was enough moss and shrubbery to keep even such beasts as mammoths well fed. By analyzing the remains of plants and pollen found buried in the tundra levels dating from this period, modern scientists have been able to estimate that the temperature in this corridor averaged 8°–10° F. in winter and close to 50° F. in July. Along the rim of the Mediterranean, on the southern side of the Alpine glacier system, there was a cold-weather temperate forest zone, where the climate may have been something like that of Denmark or northern Germany today.

The Neanderthals lived mainly in this forest zone, particularly in southern France. They sheltered themselves in caves and depended for food on hunting mammoths, rhinos, and smaller game. Those who lived at the northern frontier of this territory were the first known humans to succeed in coping with a tundra environment. The archaeological evidence indicates that the Neanderthals followed the seasonal migrations of the herds of woolly beasts. In

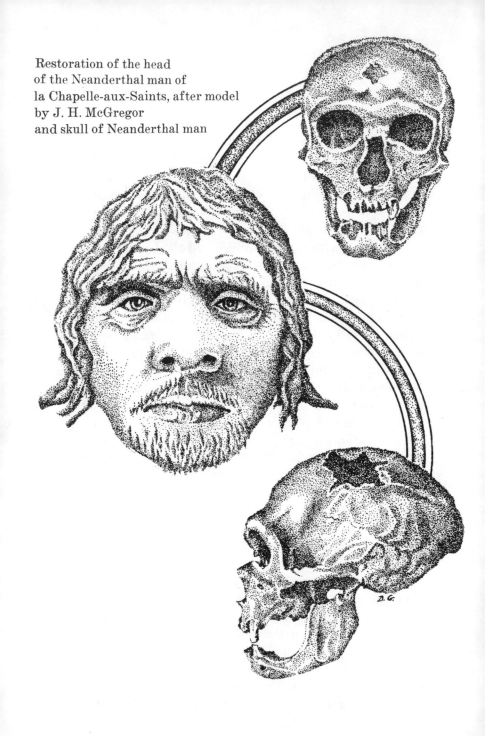

Restoration of the head
of the Neanderthal man of
la Chapelle-aux-Saints, after model
by J. H. McGregor
and skull of Neanderthal man

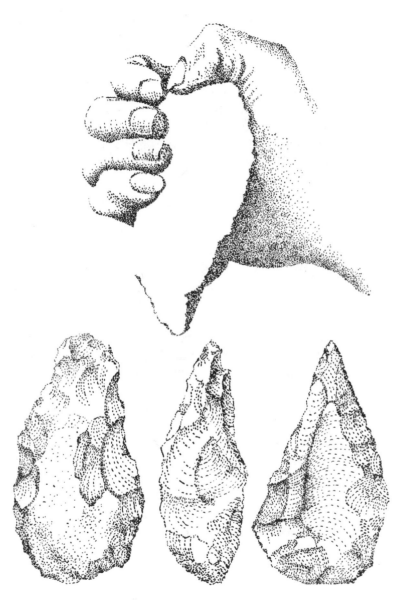

Neanderthal flint hand-axes

the summer, when the glaciers retreated a little and shrubbery sprouted, the mammoths wandered northward to graze, and the Neanderthal hunters tracked them, almost to the border of the Scandinavian glacier. When winter came, the Neanderthals retreated into the southern forests. Never before in human history had men so ably met the challenges of a hostile environment.

Then, for the fourth time, the glaciers began to dwindle. As always, there was not a sudden thaw, but rather an extremely slow process that saw the ice pulling back by a few hundred feet each year. Into Europe now came men from warmer lands to the south, roving tribes seeking new hunting grounds. These newcomers to Europe were much closer to the modern physical type of human than the Neanderthals. They were, in fact, the ancestors of contemporary European man.

There was no instant rush into Europe. The invaders moved cautiously, camping for years in one place, then pushing onward. At last they were in France and Germany, some 30,000 years ago, perhaps as early as 60,000 years ago. There they collided with the Neanderthals. We do not know what happened—whether there was a war between the two races of men, or whether the Neanderthals were absorbed peacefully into the tribes of the newcomers. We do know that the Neanderthals vanished swiftly and permanently from the world. The story is told in nearly every cave of western France. Layers of sterile sand cover the Neanderthal-style tools, and above them lie the deposits of a wholly different culture, which we call the Aurignacian, with objects of bone and horn and ivory, carved statuettes, flint tools of many shapes.

These Aurignacians are most familiar to us under the name of Cro-Magnon men, named for the rock shelter of Cro-Magnon, France, where their remains first were discovered and identified. But there were many other Aurignacian cultures—the Chatelperronians, the Gravettians, and so on—who occupied much of Europe as the ice gave way.

Europe was still relatively inhospitable when these peoples arrived. The fourth ice age was ending but it was by no means over; a sheet of mile-thick ice still covered much of northern Europe, and south of this uninhabitable ice field conditions were scarcely cheerful. The only forest trees were scrubby birches and alders that sprouted from the frozen earth. From every mountain there descended a glacier, a slowly flowing river of ice. Winters were long and wearying. Still, the weather was warmer than it had been twenty or thirty thousand years before, and was gradually getting better. And the hunting was good. The woolly mammoth and rhinoceros still lived within reach, along with the Arctic fox, the Arctic hare, and the reindeer, grazing along the fringes of the retreating sheets of ice.

As the numerous Aurignacian sites were explored by archaeologists in the latter third of the nineteenth century, a wealth of proof came forth in support of the theory that men and mammoths had lived at the same time. Not only were the bones of mammoths and the bones of human beings found in the same levels of the ground, but nearly every site yielded tools and weapon points that had been carved from mammoth bone and mammoth ivory.

Yet some conservative scientists of the late nineteenth century remained skeptical. They refused to believe in the existence of ice-age man at all. One of them was the great German biologist and archaeologist, Rudolf Virchow. When he was shown the first Neanderthal skull that was discovered, Virchow denied that it was a fossil of an ancient human type fundamentally different from modern man. Virchow simply said that the Neanderthal man must have suffered from rickets and arthritis, and that his massive brow ridges were caused by skull fractures suffered in combat.

Another highly regarded scientist who was skeptical was Japetus Steenstrup, a Danish zoologist and prehistorian. Steenstrup's interest in the animal life of the Arctic had led him to make a study of the Siberian mammoths, and then to investigate the prehistoric era when mammoths had lived. Steenstrup was convinced that mammoths had become extinct long before the appearance of humanity in the world. Confronted with such things as the tools carved from mammoth ivory, he insisted that primitive man had merely discovered and carved the fossil tusks of long-dead mammoths. As for the presence of human skeletons in the same levels as mammoth bones, that was merely the result of upheavals in the ground that mixed relics of various eras.

Steenstrup's ability to dismiss evidence in this way received its greatest test at Predmost, in Czechoslovakia. Predmost lies in a valley along a stream that flows into the Danube; lofty mountains rise nearby. Since medieval times, farmers ploughing the fertile land near this town had been discovering "giants' bones." Such finds were so common there that they quickly ceased to be remarkable, especially after it developed that the bones were not those of giants but merely those of animals that had lived before the Deluge.

About 1850, a farmer named Josef Crometschek came upon a vast deposit of bones, both animal and human, along with stone tools and ornaments. To Crometschek the bones had but one use: when ground to powder, bone makes excellent fertilizer. His workmen began grinding. But there was such a great supply that Crometschek started selling wagonloads of bones to other farmers. He went on mining this storehouse of the past for nearly thirty years before Czech archaeologists heard in 1878 of what was going on.

They persuaded Crometschek to sell his land to a museum, and by 1884 excavators were at work. Six to ten feet below the surface they found a layer of ancient deposits nearly a yard thick. It contained the ashes of innumerable fires and the bones of the great beasts of the ice age, chiefly those of the woolly mammoth.

The archaeologists soon realized that they were digging up a hunting camp that had been occupied for hundreds of years by people of the Gravettian culture. The bones of more than a thousand mammoths were found. Steenstrup, who visited Predmost in 1888, wrote, "When I saw the remains of this splendid and unique monument of nature and prehistoric culture, the reality far exceeded my expectations. Every handful of earth I picked up from these layers contained fragments of mammoths' bones."

Jindrich Wankel and Karl Maska, the archaeologists who led the Predmost work, believed that this had been a settlement of nomadic prehistoric hunters. The hunting range of the Gravettians was a narrow grassy strip, bordered on the south by the Alpine glaciers and on the north by the great Arctic ice sheet. The corridor between those two zones of ice was the grazing ground of vast herds of bison, reindeer, mammoths, and other cold-weather animals. Here on the open wind-raked plains the hunters had sought out and destroyed by the hundreds the seemingly invincible woolly mammoths. Predmost must have occupied a key position along the migration routes of the big animals; each year the hunters must have pitched camp there to lie in wait for the ponderous herds. Somehow they slew their mighty prey—perhaps by trapping mammoths in camouflaged pits and clubbing them to death, perhaps by using blazing torches to stampede the animals over cliffs. And then the huntsmen feasted.

But Japetus Steenstrup said that it had not happened that way at all. Man had not lived at the same time as these great elephants of the Arctic, he insisted. But even if he had, he would not, with his puny weapons, have been able to kill a single mammoth, let alone a thousand of the beasts. Steenstrup suggested that the mammoths of Predmost represented a herd that had been caught by a blizzard or an avalanche while moving through the mountain passes. The whole herd was buried in snow and left in an eternal deep freeze for thousands of years. Then came primitive man, discovering this fantastic cold-storage deposit and digging the mammoths out as they were needed for food.

Steenstrup's ingenious theory began to collapse in 1895, when one of the archaeologists digging at Predmost found a piece of mammoth tusk out of which a small figure of a mammoth had been carved. It showed the large fatty hump, which was still unknown from fossil evidence, though it had been observed several times on sketches found in late ice age sites. Steenstrup might have been able to say that the model for the sketch had been a frozen mammoth, but it seemed much more probable that the artist had seen live mammoths.

Then the archaeologists demonstrated that Predmost had been occupied by three successive groups of men, over a period of several centuries. Would a cache of frozen mammoths, even a thousand of them, have served a community for hundreds of years? It was easier to believe that the enormous supply of mammoth bones at Predmost was the result of generations of patient hunting. By 1900, three years after Steenstrup's death, nearly every prehistorian accepted the view that the Predmost mammoths were the victims of human hunters.

One discovery made at Predmost in 1894 showed that mammoth bones were an important building

Hunt with clubs and torches

material for the prehistoric hunters. At a depth of nine feet, the archaeologist found a mass grave whose walls were formed from the shoulder blades and skulls of mammoths. Within lay the skeletons of nearly fifty people, close together in a squatting position. The existence of this graves tells us much about these people. They took great care to protect the bodies, surrounding them with the massive bones of the beasts that yielded food, and covering the grave with a blanket of stones to ward off foxes or hyenas. Reverence for the dead indicates, perhaps, a belief in the existence of a soul, a spirit that survives the mere body. We can only guess at the philosophy of the Predmost people—who lived at least 25,000 years ago and are five times as remote from us as the builders of Egypt's pyramids—but the mass grave is a clue to their outlook.

Elsewhere at Predmost were orderly stacks of mammoth bones, obviously awaiting use by prehistoric craftsmen. Thirteen tusks were found lying together, and in another place was a pile of fifty molars. Though no dwellings have been discovered at Predmost, archaeologists working at two sites in the Soviet Union—at Megina near Kiev and at Pushkari in the Ukraine—have found the houses of similar Gravettian mammoth-hunters—with wooden walls reinforced by the huge bones of mammoths. Probably mammoth skins were used to cover the outsides of these huts, which are among the oldest known man-made structures.

There is no longer any question that men and mammoths lived together in Europe as the fourth ice age waned. The final proof was the most exciting of all: the glorious cave paintings of France and Spain, created by the artists of the Aurignacians and of the somewhat later Magdalenian culture.

The first to discover prehistoric art, as we have seen, were Lartet and Christy, digging in the rock shelters of the Dordogne in the 1860's. They found many rough plaques of bone and stone on which mammoths, reindeer, bison, and horses were skillfully drawn, as well as knives with reindeer-shaped handles and tools of bone and horn on which pictures of animals had been scratched or carved. But a far more phenomenal discovery was made in a cave at Altamira, Spain, in 1878: vivid paintings of animals, in life size, glowing with color so warm it seemed they could have been painted just days before. Here was a herd of massive humped bison, grazing, running, sleeping, standing. Here were wild horses and charging boars, prancing beasts in red and brown and black, a stupendous gallery of portraits of the creatures that once had made Europe their home. They were paintings by the hands of masters, vigorous and powerful, rendered with stunning artistic skill.

The Altamira cave was on the property of Don Marcelino de Sautuola, a Spanish aristocrat deeply interested in geology and prehistory. He had excavated in the cave several times, uncovering stone knives, awls, weapon points, and other relics of early man; but he failed to notice the wonderful paintings overhead until they were accidentally discovered by his small daughter Maria, whom he took into the cave with him one day. When Don Marcelino announced the existence of the amazing art gallery in 1880, he claimed that the paintings were the work of the prehistoric men who had left the stone age artifacts on the cave floor. But the pictures seemed too good to be true, and Don Marcelino was accused of having hired an artist to paint them. He died a bitter man, his reputation shattered.

But in 1894 a second gallery of prehistoric paintings was discovered at the cave of La Mouthe, in France. The exploration of the cave was supervised by a leading French archaeologist, Émile Rivière, and it was impossible to doubt that the paintings were genuine. It was clear now that early man, however simple his way of life had been, had been capable of creating works of art that delight the eye and dazzle the imagination.

Neither the Altamira paintings nor those of La Mouthe portrayed mammoths. But in 1901 a priest named Henri Breuil, accompanied by two other young men, entered a cave in France called Les Combarelles, and crawled for two hundred yards down a passageway a few feet high. At the end of the tunnel the explorers found a high, narrow chamber on the walls of which were engraved figures of reindeer, mammoths, bears, and lions.

At the cave of Font de Gaume, half a mile away, an even more startling array of ancient paintings awaited them: 80 bison, 40 horses, 23 mammoths, 17 reindeer, 8 wild cattle, 4 antelopes, 2 woolly rhinoceroses, a bear, a wolf, a lioness! In one place was shown a procession of mammoths walking in single file, great solemn shaggy beasts with immense tusks and lofty humps on their heads and shoulders. A short distance away was an engraving of a mammoth cub, looking like a ball of fur from which a trunk and little tusks protrude. The models for these pictures had not been frozen carcasses; even now, more than 20,000 years after they were painted, the mammoths of Font de Gaume seem to have the breath of life.

Since the beginning of the twentieth century mammoth paintings have been found in many European caves. One of the finest displays is in the cave of Pech-Merle, in southern France. The room called the Chapel of the Mammoths offers a gigantic mural some sixty feet wide, in which the mighty forms of woolly mammoths are outlined against the white background of a great arch of rock. At one side, the huge animals seem like a chain of mountains, mere humped forms in the distance. But elsewhere the mammoths are shown in remarkable detail, down to the nostrils at the tips of their trunks. The long hanging hair gives them the appearance of colossal bulk; they look like creatures from the dawn of time, mountains that walk. Strange, unforgettable, the mammoths of the cave paintings reveal to us in a unique way extinct creatures seen through the eyes of the men who dwelled among them.

MASTODONS WITH HORNS AND OTHER WONDERS

The discoveries at Predmost and in the French caves helped prehistorians greatly in their efforts to learn of the kind of world in which the mammoths had lived. Such sites yielded much information about the climate of the past and the relationship between man and mammoth toward the close of the last ice age. And the cave paintings provided an extraordinary means of seeing how these vanished elephants had looked when alive.

But it was necessary also to go on seeking more direct sources of information about the mammoths and their cousins the mastodons—specifically, the remains of the animals themselves. All during the nineteenth century the quest for fossils went on.

In the United States, a long period of unsuccessful searching followed Charles Willson Peale's acquisition of a nearly complete mastodon skeleton in 1801. Scattered bones, tusks, and grinders of mastodons and mammoths continued to turn up, but nothing that was even nearly complete. This dry spell was broken, finally, in 1841, when a curious individual named Albert Koch placed on exhibit an even more curious fossil skeleton of a creature he called *Missourium*, which made ordinary mammoths and mastodons look like pygmies.

Koch was born in Germany, and came to the United States about 1835. Nothing is known of his early life, or where he had his scientific training, if any. He always referred to himself as "Dr." Koch, but never explained how he had acquired his degree.

Settling in St. Louis, Koch opened business as a dealer in fossil specimens. He went on frequent collecting trips through the southern part of the United States, tracking down reports of fossil finds and persuading farmers to let him dig on their land. The most spectacular fossils he uncovered he placed on exhibit in a sort of traveling circus; minor pieces and scattered bones he sold to museums or universities. Whenever the public showed signs of losing interest in one of his mounted fossils, he would seek a buyer for that too.

Koch did not behave like a scientist, and many genuine scientists detested him. They regarded him accurately as a mere peddler of old bones, a charlatan showman making a profit out of the relics of the past. They resented his strongly commercial approach and sharply criticized the conclusions he attempted to draw about the fossils he discovered. Yet Koch was energetic and active, and he did dig up a great many specimens that proved to be of value.

Early in 1840 Koch unearthed the nearly complete skeleton of a mastodon in Benton County, Missouri. It lay on the shore of the small Pomme de Terre River, covered over with clay, gravel, and quicksand. This was only the second time that a mastodon skeleton in such good condition had been discovered, and thus it was an important scientific event; but Koch handled it in his own special way to make it seem even more important than it was.

His report on the excavation indicates that he went to considerable trouble to do the job scientifically. He made careful geological records of the types of soil in which the bones were lying, and even noted the well-preserved vegetable matter surrounding the skeleton. "All of the vegetable remains," he wrote, "are tropical or very low southern production. They consisted of large quantities of cypress burs, wood, and bark; a great deal of tropical cane and tropical swamp moss;" and other plant forms now found only well to the south. Evidently Missouri's climate was much milder when mastodons flourished there.

Later in 1840, Koch began to mount the Benton County skeleton for exhibition. It was a fine specimen of *Mastodon americanus,* but Koch improved it by weaving the bones of other mastodons into it, adding ribs and vertebrae until he had created a true monster. Out of two or maybe three mastodons Koch pieced together a beast he called the *Missour-*

ium, 32 feet long and 15 feet high. When he attached the tusks to the skull, he did so in such a way that they curved up and back over the animal's head like a pair of gigantic horns, instead of jutting downward and out in the proper fashion.

Koch now proceeded to haul this awe-inspiring horned mastodon all over the country on a highly profitable exhibition tour. He showed it first in St. Louis, then in Louisville, and by October, 1841, *Missourium* was on display in Philadelphia. The American Philosophical Society, that venerable and respected scientific association founded by Benjamin Franklin in 1743, heard a discussion of *Missourium* on October 15. Dr. Richard Harlan, one of America's leading authorities on fossils, told the Society that "there is now exhibiting at the Masonic Hall in Philadelphia, one of the most extensive and remarkable collections of fossil bones of extinct mammals which have hitherto been brought to light in this country." Dr. Harlan praised "the perseverance of the enterprising proprietor, Mr. Albert Koch of St. Louis, Missouri." Harlan was surprisingly gentle in dealing with the grotesque distortions and errors Koch had made in assembling the skeleton of *Missourium.* Of such things as attaching the tusks upside down to form horns, Harlan said merely that "no doubt" Koch's further researches "would enable him to rectify these."

By the end of 1841 Koch and his fossils were in London. The majestic *Missourium* went on display at Egyptian Hall in Piccadilly just before Christmas, and was sensationally successful. Such a skeleton had never been exhibited in England before; immense crowds came to view it.

One of the early visitors to Egyptian Hall was Richard Owen, England's best known anatomist and paleontologist. He eyed the monster with suspicion, observing that it seemed to have too many ribs and was put together in a peculiar way. The horns and other oddities drew Owen's critical attention also. On February 23, 1842, Owen read a paper on Koch's fossil at a meeting of the Geological Society of London. He disputed Koch's claim of having discovered a new giant animal, saying that *Missourium* was simply a mastodon that had been mounted incorrectly. Koch was bold enough to challenge the great scientist on his home grounds; on April 6, 1842, he addressed the Geological Society to insist that he had indeed unearthed a previously unknown genus.

The debate did not hurt business at Koch's fossil sideshow. Month after month the customers thronged into Egyptian Hall. Not until the summer of 1843 did Koch close his London show and take his fossils on tour again. He showed them in Ireland and then in Germany, where they aroused even greater interest than they had in England.

In May, 1844, Koch returned to the United States. On his way back from Germany he stopped in London and sold *Missourium* and some of his other fossils to the British Museum. For the mastodon he received an extraordinary price: $2000 down, and $1000 a year for the rest of his life. (This arrangement brought Koch $23,000 before his death in 1866.) Immediately after the purchase, British Museum paleontologists took the monster apart, stripping away the extra bones and putting the tusks where they belonged. The dehorned skeleton, correctly labeled *Mastodon americanus*, is still to be seen in the gallery of fossil mammals of the British Museum's natural history collection at South Kensington. It is one of the finest mastodon fossils in existence.

The supply of such fossils was considerably increased in October, 1844, by a farmer of Hackettstown, New Jersey. While digging the rich mud from a small pond he had recently drained, he came upon the partial skeletons of five mastodons lying close together: one large male, two younger males, a female, and a calf. The skeletons were in poor condition and crumbled when exposed to the air, but about ten feet from them was a sixth skeleton, almost complete, which was excavated unharmed and purchased by Harvard University's museum of anatomy.

These mastodons had been lying in boggy ground for thousands of years. The water of bogs often contains humic acid, which has a preserving effect on organic matter; and so the Hackettstown site contained not only skeletons but the remains of plants and shrubs of the same age as the mastodons, and even some of the food the animals had eaten before being trapped in the bog. Dr. John C. Warren of Harvard, one of the foremost medical men of his time and also an outstanding authority on mastodons, visited the site and wrote this description:

> The bones were found in a basin. On the top of the stratum in which they occurred

was about a foot of vegetable deposit, formed of decayed leaves, etc., then about six inches of whitish sand, mixed with vegetable matter, and below this a deposit which, Mr. Ayers (the owner of the farm) says, when first opened was of a yellowish color. . . . Exposure to the weather has changed its color to the dull bluish black of swamp-earth, which it seems to be mixed with; there are great quantities of vegetable remains, principally of marsh plants, with scattered fragments of branches of trees, etc. . . . Between the ribs of two or three of the skeletons was a considerable quantity of what Mr. Ayers describes as resembling coarse-chopped straw, mixed with fragments of sticks; no doubt the contents of the stomach. . . . I regretted very much that my knowledge was not sufficient to determine the species of the plants of which so many portions remain, but I thought I recognized some which are now growing in the neighboring marshes, such as flags, cat-tails, etc.

In August, 1845, one of the most splendid mastodons ever found came to light near Newburgh, New York. Here, too, boggy conditions had preserved ancient vegetable matter, four or five bushels of it, found in a twisted pattern following what must have been the outline of the mastodon's intestines. Once more Dr. Warren of Harvard hurried to the discovery site. Warren purchased the Newburgh skeleton, which thereafter was known as the Warren mastodon, and for many years it remained on display at Harvard. (In 1846 he also bought the second, incomplete mastodon skeleton that once had been in the Peale Museum, which had passed into the possession of the showman P. T. Barnum. The more famous first Peale mastodon was sold to a museum in Germany.)

Through a quite innocent error in mounting, the Warren mastodon came out nearly eighteen feet high at the shoulders when it was put together, making it much larger than any mastodon previously found, or any known elephant. This happened because all hoofed animals, including elephants and mastodons, lack collarbones; the bones of their front limbs are not firmly connected to other parts of their skeletons except at the shoulderblades. By changing the angle of the slope of the back, it is possible to increase the height of an elephant or mastodon skeleton by as much as three feet. When the American Museum of Natural History in New York bought the Warren mastodon in 1906, the error in mounting was discovered. The skeleton was remounted to stand 14 feet 11 inches high—even then an extraordinary sight. It can still be seen at the museum today.

Mastodon skeletons and bones continued to turn up fairly regularly in the United States all during the nineteenth century, and mammoth fossils as well. They are occasionally discovered during construction work to this day. As the number of fossils rose, it became apparent that there had been many different species of mastodons and mammoths over the years, some of them quite strange in appearance, with shovel-shaped tusks or with extra tusks in their lower jaws. Late in the nineteenth century the first attempts were made to classify the numerous mastodon and mammoth types and to discern the pattern that the process of evolution had followed in changing the forms of these huge creatures.

At the same time scientists looked hopefully toward the world's greatest storehouse of mammoth fossils, Siberia, for some new revelation of how living mammoths had looked. The Adams mammoth of 1806 was well remembered; perhaps another complete frozen carcass would come to light one day. An even fainter hope still glowed: possibly a herd of live mammoths might be found somewhere in Siberia's desolate northland!

It was hard to accept the fact that mammoths and mastodons were totally extinct. As early as 1803, Rembrandt Peale had declared, "We are forced to submit to concurring facts as the voice of God: the bones exist—the animals do not!" Even so, explorers in the western United States kept their eyes out for live mastodons for many years thereafter, without any luck. In Siberia, which was larger and had been even less thoroughly explored, the occasional discoveries of frozen mammoths encouraged the hope that some unfrozen ones still roamed. Another possibility was Alaska, just across the Bering Strait from Siberia, and very similar in climate. Mammoth bones were first discovered there in 1816, and the finders detected the smell of decaying flesh at the site, as though the mammoths had died quite recently.

Mammoth carcasses continued to turn up in Siberia, but always under frustrating circumstances for science. In 1839, spring rains exposed the complete body of a frozen mammoth on the shore of a lake about fifty miles from the Arctic Ocean. Samoyed tribesmen found it and cut off one of its tusks for sale. But by the time Russian scientists learned of the find in 1842, most of the mammoth had decayed or been eaten by dogs. Its skeleton, some portions of red, stiff hair, and about six pounds of flesh were salvaged and taken to a museum in Moscow.

In 1843 a half-grown mammoth's carcass was found on the banks of the River Taimyr in western Siberia, but it, too, decayed before it could be examined closely. Other mammoths were discovered in 1860, 1865, 1867, and 1868, but in each case scientists were unable to reach them in time to inspect or preserve the soft parts. Nor were any live mammoths seen. The Yukaghir tribesmen of eastern Siberia offered a Russian scientific expedition of the late nineteenth century this explanation of why the mammoth had vanished:

"The creation of the mammoth was a blunder of the Superior Being. In creating such an enormous animal, the Creator did not take into consideration the size of the earth and its resources. The earth could not stand the weight of the mammoth and its vegetation was not sufficient to feed the mammoth race. The mammoth fed on tree trunks which he ground with his teeth, and in a short time the whole north of Siberia was deprived of trees. Hence is the origin of the northern tundra. In the beginning the earth had the form of an even plain, but by his weight the monster animal in moving about caused the formation of valleys and ravines in which rivers originated. In swampy or sandy places the mammoth sank into the ground and disappeared under the earth, where he froze during the winter. Often in the hole over him water gathered into a lake. In this way the mammoth gradually disappeared from the earth's surface. This is why now whole cadavers of the animal are to be found in the frozen soil.''

A few hundred miles to the east on the Alaskan coast, the Chuklukmiut Eskimos told a somewhat similar story. They called the mammoth *kilu kpuk,* "the kilu whale." These whales, they said, were driven from the water by sea-monsters and forced to live on shore, but they were too heavy and sank into the ground. However, they were able to move their tusks sideways in their sockets, and used them like shears to cut tunnels for themselves under the earth.

Although mammoth bones had occasionally been found in Alaska, and the Alaskan Eskimos knew and made use of mammoth ivory, no frozen mammoth carcasses had ever been discovered there. But the Russians, who owned Alaska until 1867, never gave up hope that they might find frozen or even live mammoths in that vast territory. After the purchase of Alaska by the United States, American explorers and scientists continued the quest.

Late in the nineteenth century, a naturalist named C. H. Townsend, who worked for the U. S. Fish Commission, made a tour of Alaska's coast. At one port in the far north Eskimos offered articles made of mammoth ivory for barter. This led Townsend to show the Eskimos a picture of the Adams mammoth in a book he had brought along, asking them if they had ever seen anything like that. He also drew a sketch of a mammoth which he gave to them.

The sketch passed from hand to hand; the Eskimos copied it and sent it to inland tribes; soon the subject of mammoths was under discussion across a good deal of Alaska, and the Eskimos, eager to please, obligingly invented tales of huge beasts. Rumors of living mammoths began to filter back to the white hunters and trappers on the coast, and before long American newspapers were carrying stories on the mammoths that supposedly had been seen in Alaska. Then, in October, 1899, *McClure's*, a popular magazine of the day, carried a short piece by one Henry Tukeman called "The Killing of the Mammoth." It told how the narrator and a young Alaskan Indian named Paul had entered a remote part of Alaska where they found and killed the last surviving mammoth in the world. Every detail was vividly described, down to the exciting final moments when the enraged beast collapsed before the repeated blasts of the hunters' rifles. The author said that the "generous but eccentric millionaire, Horace P. Conradi," had contributed the immense sum needed to bring the great beast's skeleton and hide back to civilization; thanks to Mr. Conradi, the stuffed and mounted mammoth could now be seen at the Smithsonian Institution in Washington.

For weeks afterward, the Smithsonian's officials were kept busy denying that they had a stuffed mammoth on the premises. For there was no such person as Horace P. Conradi and there had been no mammoth hunt in Alaska. Henry Tukeman's story was simply a work of fiction, though *McClure's* had not bothered to identify it as one. People were so eager to believe that mammoths still lived that they insisted on taking the story for a factual account.

Not long afterward, though, exciting news came out of Siberia—not of a live mammoth, but of the next best thing, a frozen one that was still nearly complete.

In August, 1900, some men of the Lamut tribe were hunting near the Beresovka River in northeastern Siberia. They were following the track of an elk when suddenly one of the hunting dogs sniffed the air, veered, and went off in a new direction. Semen Tarabykin, the Lamut who owned the dog, followed the animal, which led him to a place where the well-preserved head of a mammoth was sticking out of the frozen ground. Tarabykin, who believed that to find a mammoth carcass meant bad luck and disease, hurried away at once, exactly as Ossip Shumakhov had done in the same situation 101 years before. But the next day, after conferring with two friends, Tarabykin decided to go back. All three went to the mammoth site and pulled free one of the tusks. Tarabykin noticed that wolves had come during the night and had gnawed the flesh of the mammoth's exposed head and back.

Later in the year Tarabykin sold the tusk to a Cossack trader named Yavlovski, who asked him where he had obtained it. Tarabykin told him the story of the mammoth. Yavlovski, knowing that the Russian Academy of Sciences paid large rewards for information about well-preserved mammoth remains, arranged for the Lamut to take him to see the animal. In November, 1900, Tarabykin led Yavlovksi to the mammoth. The trader cut off a few fragments of skin as proof of the discovery, and forwarded them along with the tusk to the governor of the district. The governor shipped the parcel to distant St. Petersburg; it reached the Academy of Sciences in April of 1901.

The Academy voted to spend 16,300 rubles—then about $8,000—on an expedition to recover the Beresovka River mammoth. Dr. Otto Herz, the curator of the Academy's department of zoology, was placed in charge of the expedition, although Herz' specialty was insects, not mammoths. He was to be accompanied by D. P. Sevastianov, a geologist, and E. W. Pfizenmayer, a young German-born taxidermist—an expert in the mounting of animal specimens. They set out on their long eastward journey at the beginning of May, 1901.

The trip was an extraordinary ordeal. Their first goal was Yakutsk, in eastern Siberia, the largest town in that desolate part of the world. Yakutsk was 2,000 miles from the place where the mammoth had been found, but it was the only town in the eastern half of Siberia where the scientists could hire the men and buy the equipment they required for their work. By train, by cart, by boat, and by river steamer, the explorers journeyed deep into Asia, reaching Yakutsk in June, 1901. There Herz acquired the things he needed: biscuits, dried meat, warm blankets, sheepskin jackets, steel tools specially made for digging in frozen ground, mosquito netting, and a folding boat of leather that could be converted into a tent.

Everything was packed in leather sacks or in crates covered with hides, so there would be no damage from rain or from the water of rivers and streams. The expedition would be traveling in the Siberian summer, when a tremendous thaw sends short-lived torrents cascading through the tundra.

Because it was summer, they could not use sledges, the customary means of swift transportation in Siberia. The heat was turning great stretches of the tundra into a sea of mud, and sledges would bog down before they had gone twenty yards. The travelers would have to go on horseback, and in some places on foot.

Accompanied by two local guides, they set out northward on June 20. They went a short way by river steamer; then the real trek began. Their horses plodded through swampy country that limited progress to 15 to 25 miles a day. In many places the men had to dismount and lead the horses over sloppy, treacherous muddy terrain. Rivers and creeks overflowed, so that the horses occasionally waded belly-deep in muddy water. After nineteen days of such travel they reached Verkhoyansk, six hundred miles from Yakutsk, the place where they had arranged to obtain fresh horses.

In winter, Verkhoyansk is one of the coldest places in the world, and a temperature of 50° below zero is nothing unusual. But in July it is afflicted by virtually tropical heat and humidity. Herz, Pfizenmayer, and Sevastianov found themselves in a world of mud and mosquitoes. Nor were enough horses available for the whole group, and it became necessary to split up. On July 11, Herz started out toward the town of Sredne Kolymsk, where the discoverer of the mammoth lived. He took with him two guides, six horses, and part of the baggage. Pfizenmayer and Sevastianov were to follow five days later, with the rest of the baggage, once additional horses became available.

Herz had an uneventful journey to Sredne Kolymsk, but the second group experienced unending troubles. Bogs, lakes, and wild, swollen rivers sent them on long detours; the rain grew heavier from day to day; the horses became mired in deep mud and exhausted themselves trying to get free. By day the heat was unbearable, and at night the temperatures dropped as low as 9°F. On July 29, the travelers were caught in a sudden daytime snowstorm that threatened to halt them altogether, but after a while it turned to heavy rain.

They averaged less than fifteen miles a day, though they were on the road fourteen hours or more. Long rest periods became necessary both for the men and the horses. Suffering intensely, they forced themselves onward, and when they reached Sredne Kolymsk on September 2 the geologist Sevastianov was in such a state of collapse that Pfizenmayer thought he would die. It had taken a month and a half to cover the 1300 miles from Verkhoyansk.

They learned that Herz had left Sredne Kolymsk

on August 29, to make the final two hundred-mile leg of the journey to the mammoth. After a week's rest, Pfizenmayer and Sevastianov followed Herz' route. Summer was over now; snowstorms several days long halted them more than once. Herz, too, was having his troubles with the snow. Huge drifts obliterated all landmarks and the Siberian guides did not dare to move onward. He finally reached the mammoth site in the second week of September, and built a hut there. Pfizenmayer and Sevastianov still were struggling along behind him. Herz sent a man back to tell them where he was; but when Sevastianov learned that deep snow covered the entire countryside, he decided that as a geologist he would have nothing to do, and he went back to Sredne Kolymsk. Pfizenmayer continued forward as soon as the weather would permit, and joined Herz at last about the middle of September.

The mammoth, though, made all the hardships worthwhile. It was still nearly complete, frozen into the side of a cliff that had been opened by a landslide. Wild animals had nibbled away much of its trunk, the skin of its head, and part of one foreleg but the rest of the mammoth remained sealed in a block of ice.

The expedition began to clear away the soil, rock, and ice that gripped the huge beast's body. They freed the head first, and, at a depth of twenty-seven inches, they came to the left foreleg, still covered with long reddish hair. Then they uncovered the right hind leg. From the position in which the mammoth lay, it now became possible to guess at the way the animal had met its death. It was sitting on its haunches in a tumbled-looking way, with its right hind leg thrust forward and its front limbs flexed as if grasping at the ground. The animal must have been feeding on the tundra plants in freshly fallen snow, and had stepped out onto a thin crust of recent ice covering a deep crevasse. Plunging in, it was badly injured by its fall—examination of the skeleton later showed that the mammoth had broken its right foreleg and its pelvis—but still it fought to lift itself from the pit. In its dying struggles the animal pulled tons of loose snow down on itself, until it was buried. And there it remained, hidden and perfectly preserved, for an incredible length of time.

The mammoth's position also indicated what had inspired the Siberian myths about giant underground ''rats.'' With its huge front legs hooked over the edge of the crevasse, the mammoth seemed like some monstrous and bizarre creature trying to climb up from the depths of the earth.

Problems arose as Herz sought to uncover his unique specimen. Winter was closing in, and chipping away the frozen, iron-hard soil and ice about the mammoth became a terribly strenuous task. He halted excavation for twelve days while a hut was built over the site. Now the men could work in heated surroundings; but this created difficulties too, for the bacteria of decay began to flourish in the thawing mammoth. The stench that came from the rotting corpse was all but intolerable.

They forced themselves to go on, and by early October the mammoth stood completely free from its tomb. Pfizenmayer now started to dissect the animal so it could be shipped back to Russia for study. He carefully peeled back the thick, hairy hide to remove the bones and organs beneath. He separated the shoulderblades, the ribs, and then the immense stomach, which still contained more than thirty pounds of undigested food. From this and from the food that had still been in the mammoth's mouth when death came, botanists were able to determine its diet: wild flowers, mosses, herbs, grasses, and the boughs of such tundra shrubs as dwarfed larch, fir, and pine. The presence of seeds showed that the mammoth had died in the autumn. Pfizenmayer wrote, "The mammoth's food is composed of the same plants that still grow today in the close neighborhood of the site of the discovery, plants that we have gathered and preserved in order to compare them."

The mammoth's hide was covered with dark red hair four to five inches in length; there was a yellow-brown undercoat, about an inch long. Beneath the hide was a layer of fat three to four inches thick. Both the head and the shoulders were topped with much thicker masses of fat, giving the mammoth the humped appearance it bore in prehistoric carvings and paintings. The presence of these humps on the Beresovka mammoth was a striking confirmation that the cave art was truly the work of ancient man.

When Pfizenmayer cut through the fat over the mammoth's hind legs, he saw dark red, fresh-looking meat. It could have been the meat of an animal killed only a short while before. The explorers considered the idea of cooking mammoth steaks for themselves, but could not quite bring themselves to sample the age-old meat. However, the expedition's pack-dogs found its taste first-rate.

The taxidermist also discovered a large mass of clotted blood near the mammoth's stomach. He salvaged this for laboratory examination, and it proved quite valuable. It is possible to determine relationships among animals by blood tests; the blood of related animals will produce a similar reaction in such a test, and the blood of unrelated animals will not. When the Beresovka mammoth's blood was tested it showed a close relationship between Siberian mammoths and modern Asian elephants. But African elephants proved to be much more distantly linked to mammoths.

By the middle of October the Beresovka mammoth had been skinned and packed. Skeleton, hide, and internal organs would all be shipped to the Academy of Sciences in St. Petersburg; only the meat would be left behind, except for some sample pieces. Ten sledges were needed to carry the mammoth on the 2000-mile journey back to Yakutsk, and then on the 1850-mile trip from Yakutsk to the central Siberian city of Irkutsk, where it would be loaded aboard the train to Russia.

Dogs and horses drew the sledges for the first 200 miles. Then, as the full harshness of winter began to descend, the horses were replaced by reindeer for the next 1300-mile stretch. Snowstorms and blizzards were almost daily events, and the temperature rarely rose as high as the zero mark. Frequently they had to march on foot through the steep drifts. Once, while they were hiking in a blinding storm, Herz noticed a little package lying in the snow; it had been dropped by the man in front of him, and contained such priceless things as the mammoth's hair, its tongue, and the food found between its teeth.

Despite all hardships they were able to make better time in this harsh winter weather than they had in the muddy summer. By Christmas Eve Pfizenmayer was in Yakutsk; Herz, who had been held up by blizzards, arrived on January 6, 1902, and after a brief rest they set out for Irkutsk, averaging more than 100 miles a day on this part of the journey. A special post office train was waiting to carry the mammoth to St. Petersburg as fast as possible. By March, 1902, the Academy of Sciences had its mammoth.

A team of scientists went to work on the internal organs, while taxidermists under Pfizenmayer's direction stuffed and mounted the mammoth's skin in the half-sitting position in which the animal had died. The stuffed mammoth and its skeleton went on display side by side in the Academy of Science's zoology museum, where they still may be seen, not far from the skeleton of the Adams mammoth of 1806.

A discovery nearly rivaling the Beresovka one was made in 1948 on the Taimyr Peninsula in western Siberia: the skeleton of a large mammoth, with fragments of muscle, tendons, and hair attached. It was the most complete mammoth skeleton ever found, although the skin and internal organs were gone and only some scraps of muscle, tendons, and hair remained. But the Academy of Sciences expedition that examined the mammoth site came away with important information on the era in which the mammoth had lived. The skeleton was buried amid remains of ancient birch and willow trees, which today cannot grow as far north as the Taimyr Peninsula. Evidently the ice age had already ended at the time of this mammoth's death, and Siberia's climate was 4°–7°F. warmer than it is now, with vegetation found a hundred miles or more farther to the north than today.

So far only one frozen mammoth carcass has been discovered in Alaska, although beyond much doubt others lie hidden in the permafrost. In 1948, miners working near Fairbanks, Alaska, uncovered a baby mammoth about one year old. The high-pressure hydraulic jets used to cut through the frozen muck destroyed everything but the trunk, the face, and one forelimb before the presence of the little mammoth was noticed. The remains were shipped to the American Museum of Natural History in New York, and for a while were displayed in a glass-topped freezer chest in the museum's main lobby.

A few years after the discovery of the Alaskan mammoth, the carbon-14 method of dating the past came into general use. This technique employs radioactive isotopes to reveal the age of samples of wood, bone, shell, and other organic materials up to about 50,000 years old. A sample of skin and flesh from the baby mammoth received the carbon-14 test and proved to be about 21,300 years old.

Later, a piece of skin from the Adams mammoth excavated in 1806 received the same test. It showed that the mammoth had died more than 30,000 years ago. The Beresovka mammoth also lived more than 30,000 years ago. The bitter cold of the Arctic has given scientists a remarkable treasure: not merely the skeletons of extinct animals, but even their hair, muscles, internal organs, blood vessels, skin, tongues, brains, and eyes—preserved across hundreds of centuries and enabling us to develop an astonishingly complete picture of what these great beasts were like when they walked the earth.

THE FAMILY TREE OF THE ELEPHANTS

Aside from the dinosaurs, mammoths and mastodons are probably the best known of prehistoric animals, and the ones that have stirred most interest among both scientists and laymen. And, thanks to the many fossil discoveries, the finds of frozen carcasses, and the paintings in the caves, we are today able to provide a remarkable array of facts about these extinct behemoths.

We know that mammoths were hairy elephants that occupied much of the northern half of the globe, living not only in Siberia but in northern Europe as well, and in many areas of North America. The first mammoths evolved out of earlier elephant forms about two million years ago, before the first of the four ice ages. During each advance of the glaciers, mammoths were able to penetrate deep into southerly regions normally too warm for them. When the ice retreated, so did the mammoths, pulling back into the chilly terrain they preferred. This geographical seesaw continued until about 10,000 years ago. Then the most recent ice age reached its end and the world's climate began to grow warmer in a fairly steady rise; and about the same time the mammoths became extinct, for reasons that—as we shall see—are not yet well understood.

Different types of mammoths existed in different parts of the world. Zoologists have had no end of difficulty in classifying these varieties and in giving them scientific names. As far back as 1799, Johann Blumenbach decreed that mammoths belonged in the same genus as modern elephants, and gave them the Latin name of *Elephas primigenius,* "the first-born elephant." Some scientists still use this as the scientific name of the mammoth.

But it developed that the mammoths found in southern Europe were larger than those found in northern Europe and Siberia, and that the mammoths of North America were even larger. An attempt was made to distinguish among these by giving them separate species names. The Siberian mammoth became *Elephas beresovkius* (after the Beresovka specimen), the southern European mammoth was called *Elephas meridionalis,* and the giant North American mammoth *Elephas imperator.*

In the twentieth century came another upheaval of names. Now it was decided to take all the mammoths out of the genus *Elephas,* which would be reserved only for the modern Asian elephant. They would be given a new generic name to signify that they were extinct. Unfortunately, the scientists could not agree on the new name. One faction wanted to put all the mammoths into the genus *Mammuthus*. Another group proposed *Mammonteus*. A different approach was to call the woolly mammoth of the north *Mammuthus primigenius* and to class the other types of mammoths in altogether different genera, such as *Archidiskodon* and *Parelephas*.

The confusion remains unresolved. It is possible to see the same kind of skeleton labeled *Elephas imperator, Mammuthus imperator*, and *Archidiskodon imperator* in three different textbooks of zoology. Most of us do not need to let this muddle of Latin terms trouble the mind, though it does indicate the extreme complexities that can arise in the effort to classify animals in some kind of orderly fashion. Whatever the names used, though, we should know that mammoths did come in several fairly distinct forms.

The woolly mammoth of the north, usually called *Elephas primigenius* or *Mammuthus primigenius,* is the form about which the most is known, since this is the only type of mammoth whose complete frozen carcasses have survived into our time. Contrary to popular belief, this mammoth was not particularly large. In fact, it was rather small, as elephants go.

Full-grown male African elephants of today average 10 to 11 feet in height at the shoulder and weigh 5 to 7 tons; the biggest one ever known, killed in 1955 and now in the Smithsonian Institution in Washington, stood 13 feet 2 inches and weighed 12 tons. Asian elephants of today are somewhat smaller, the males standing 8 to 9 feet high, with the record height reported to be 10 feet 8 inches.

The 1806 Adams mammoth also stood 10 feet 8 inches at the shoulder, but this was one of the biggest mammoths ever found in Siberia. More typical, perhaps, was the Beresovka mammoth, 8 feet 10 inches tall. The woolly mammoths were probably no bigger on the average than modern Asian elephants, and were a good deal smaller than modern African elephants. However, the thick coating of hair of the northern mammoths must have made them seem more bulky than they really were.

Woolly mammoths reached somewhat greater heights in Europe than they attained in Siberia. A skeleton found in Austria and now in a German museum stands 12 feet 10 inches high. Germany also had a giant mammoth, similar to the Siberian mammoth in all but size, but usually classed as a separate subspecies: *Elephas* (or *Mammuthus*) *primigenius fraasi*. Members of this subspecies reached heights of 14 feet 4 inches, 3 to 4 feet taller than the big African elephants of today and 4 to 5 feet taller than the average Siberian mammoth. The hump of this giant German mammoth may have added another foot or two to its height.

The mammoth's dense fur, forming an overcoat hanging almost to the ground, was one of the means by which this animal withstood the extreme cold of the ice-age world. A fine undercoat of inch-long hair covered the mammoth's entire body. Above this was a much thicker layer of hair, 4 to 6 inches long on the lower part of the legs, and up to a foot and a half in length on the back and sides of the body. During the summer the mammoth shed much of its fur, retaining a coat only a few inches long.

The tail of the mammoth was quite short, and its ears were unusually small, smaller even than those of modern Asian elephants. These features also were adaptations to the cold. The smaller the ears and tail are, the less exposure of skin surfaces to the icy air, and the less body heat lost through radia tion. Tufts of hair provided extra insulation for the mammoth's ears and tail.

The trunk also was hairy, and its tip was of an unusual design. The Asian elephant of today has a finger-like projection at the lower edge of its trunk-tip, with which it grasps small objects and inspects the ground. African elephants have two such "fingers," one above the nostrils and one below them. But a prehistoric picture from the cave of Les Combarelles clearly shows the tip of a mammoth's trunk with a "finger" above and a wide flap-like projection below, as though to serve as a lid covering the nostrils in severely cold weather. The accuracy of this portrait was confirmed in 1924, when for the first time a mammoth carcass was found in Siberia with the tip of the trunk still intact.

Another unusual feature of the woolly mammoth was its pair of fatty humps, one atop the head and the other on the shoulders. The effect of these two bulges was to give the mammoth a highly distinctive outline, with the back rising steeply toward the peak of the hump, then dropping just as steeply to create a V-shaped notch just behind the high-rising head. Presumably these humps allowed the mammoth to store energy in the form of fat as an emergency reserve for a hard winter.

The mammoth's most startling and memorable feature was its mighty tusks. They came out of the front of the skull fairly close together, grew forward and downward, curving away from each other and then back in again, in some cases forming a complete circle with the tips crossing. Tusks 10 to 12 feet long were nothing extraordinary, and lengths of up to 16 feet have been recorded. There is no authenticated record of an African elephant with tusks as long as 12 feet, and those of Asian elephants are usually much smaller.

The great puzzle about the mammoth's colossal tusks is what use the animal could have had for them. Tusks that cross or touch at the tips would not be very good in fighting; the mammoth might be able to crush an enemy with them, but he would never be able to spear one. Nor would such tusks serve very well for digging up roots, as modern elephants often do with theirs. The crossed tusks of mammoth fossils baffled the experts trying to reassemble their skeletons, and frequently the tusks were mounted with the left one where the right belonged, and vice versa. That way the tips of the tusks pointed outward in a more deadly fashion. It was a natural error to make; but the cave paintings and the frozen carcasses leave no doubt that the mammoth's tusks curved inward.

Evolution rarely provides an animal with a completely useless organ, or allows it to keep an organ that has lost its function. If those fantastic tusks were merely a burden, offering no advantage at all, they would probably have vanished over the course of time.

Occasionally evolution does work in reverse, so to speak, transforming a useful organ into something apparently useless. This is generally a sign of the coming extinction of a species. In its old age, often, a species will develop bizarre ornaments—crests, spines, weird enlargements of horns or antlers. Apparently this represents a final flourish of biological creativity before the species' disappearance. The late dinosaurs were particularly notable for their grotesque spikes and knobs and protuberances. The strange tusks of the mammoth may have been the signal that the end was drawing near for this particular line of elephants.

A more likely explanation, though, is that the crossed tusks were quite useful to the mammoth in its particular environment. We know from the evidence of the stomach contents of the Beresovka mammoth that mammoths lived on plants and shrubs, just as elephants do today. We also know that the preferred habitat of the mammoth was the tundra country of the north. It never was a true Arctic animal like the walrus or the polar bear. The walrus eats shellfish and other seafood, and the polar bear hunts seals and fish; but the mammoth, being a vegetarian requiring enormous quantities of food a day, had to live where plants grew. The Arctic snowfields could never support a mammoth's needs.

In the tundra, however, heavy snowfalls occur frequently, ten or eleven months of the year. The mammoth must have needed a way of digging down through drifts many feet deep in order to reach the dwarf birch, willow, heather, grasses, and other plants on which it fed. The great curved tusks would have made excellent snowplows. Bending forward and swinging its head from side to side, the mammoth could easily sweep away the snow. In warmer weather, it might have used the bumper-like tusks to push aside bushes, tough shrubs, or small trees to get at the tender grasses close to the ground.

Even with built-in snowplows, though, mammoths could not have survived for long in the Siberian tundra where their frozen carcasses have been found, if the climate of that tundra was anything like what it is today. Much of the territory that is richest in mammoth bones and carcasses is treeless and almost permanently snow-covered in modern times; but the Beresovka find and several similar ones show that in the era of the mammoths the conditions there were less harsh. What is bleak tundra today was then the kind of marshy cold-weather forest of pine and birch that the Siberians call *taiga*. The forests and meadows of the taiga reached far to the north, almost to the Arctic Ocean, at least in the mild periods between the glacial epochs. At such times, mammoths spent their winters in the southern Siberian taiga, and during the summers migrated north to avoid heat and insects, going into the briefly blooming zone of the Arctic's rim.

On the other hand, during the worst years of the

Mammoth using tusks to push away shrubs

ice ages, Siberia must have been uninhabitable even for mammoths. All the climatic zones were pushed southward; what now is tundra was covered by Arctic glaciers, what now is taiga was tundra, and what now is temperate-zone oak-and-maple forest was then taiga. In these hard times the woolly mammoths wandered into such countries as France and Germany in search of the cold but not Arctic environment they needed. The tundra and the taiga were its habitat, and as the cycles of climate shifted, the mammoths of the north followed that habitat about.

The other species of mammoths preferred temperate or even warm climates. They were bigger than their northern cousin—bigger, indeed, than any other kind of elephant. We do not know how hairy they were, because they did not live in regions where their frozen carcasses could be preserved, but there is no reason to think that they had the distinctive shaggy coats of the Siberian mammoth. More likely the mammoths of temperate zones had light coats of hair, and those of warm lands were as hairless as modern elephants.

Three main features distinguish all these mammoths from the rest of the elephant tribe: their bones, their teeth, and their tusks. Their bones were more massive, and differed from other elephants in such things as the number of ribs and the shape of the skull. Their molar teeth, although they were the flat grinders typical of all elephant species, had an unusually large number of enamel ridges. And their tusks were extremely long, curving inward so that the tips often met. (The existence of crossed-tip tusks on mammoths of warm lands is one of the chief arguments against the "snowplow" theory.)

The non-woolly mammoths appeared earlier than the woolly mammoths, evolving out of earlier elephant forms almost two million years ago. Although Johann Blumenbach in 1799 thought the woolly mammoth was the "first-born elephant," it was actually a latecomer among elephant species. To understand where the mammoths stand in relation to other elephants, we have to look back along a family tree that stretches across some 40 million years.

At the base of the family tree we find a small animal known as *Moeritherium,* which scarcely looked like an elephant at all. It was an animal no bigger than a pig, with neither tusks nor a trunk, that lived in Egypt. About sixty miles southwest of Cairo there is a desert called the Fayum, which in ancient times was the site of a swampy lake called Lake Moeris. Here, in the early years of the twentieth century, Charles W. Andrews of the British Museum of Natural History found the fossil skeleton of this earliest known ancestral elephant, which he named *Moeritherium,* "Moeris animal," after the vanished lake.

Moeritherium stood about two feet high, with a long, low skull and stocky body. The structure of its jaws shows that it did not have a trunk, although it seems likely that it had a short flexible snout like that of the modern tapir of South America and Asia. (Since trunks and snouts have no bones to become fossilized, it is difficult to know exactly what forms they took on prehistoric animals.) *Moerither-*

ium had both grinding teeth (molars) and biting teeth (incisors). One of its three pairs of incisors was larger than the others, and these oversized teeth must have been useful in helping *Moeritherium* dig up reeds and other marsh plants. The animal probably spent most of its time browsing in swampy vegetation, and may have looked and acted something like a pygmy hippopotamus.

From the Fayum also came the fossil of the animal that evolved out of *Moeritherium*. Scientists call it *Paleomastodon,* "the ancient mastodon." It lived about five million years after *Moeritherium,* and was somewhat larger, standing about four feet high. *Paleomastodon's* lower jaw shows some interesting evolutionary changes; it juts forward, and from it thrust two horizontal tusks, front teeth which have flattened out and become quite lengthy. These must have been used like spades or shovels to dig up plants. Also, the nostril openings on *Paleomastodon's* skull are much higher on the face than on *Moeritherium*. This tells scientists that *Paleomastodon* must have had at least the beginnings of a trunk. An elephant's trunk is really an enlarged and lengthened nose, equipped with a complex array of muscles. It can drink through the trunk by drawing water into the two inner passages and squirting it into its mouth; it can smell and feel with the trunk, it can grasp and hold things, and it can shovel food into its mouth with it. Since an elephant's head is so massive, its neck must be thick and short to support it, and thus the head cannot bend very far toward the ground to pick up food, but the trunk serves extremely well to collect and lift things for it.

The handy trunk enabled *Paleomastodon* to thrive; some later forms reached heights of more than seven feet, nearly as big as modern elephants. The combination of tusks for scooping and a trunk for lifting worked so well that the process of evolution continued to lengthen both. Two of the upper teeth began to sprout into tusks as well. New forms called *Tetrabelodon* and *Trilophodon* now evolved and spread rapidly to many parts of the world, some twenty to thirty million years ago. These were animals the size of Asian elephants, with four tusks, long trunks, and long lower jaws. One form found in Nebraska had a jaw six feet long! However, these tremendously extended jaws got in the way of the trunk, which was unable to move freely, and the next stage in evolution was the gradual shortening of the jaw. At last the jaw became quite short and the trunk dangled freely.

There were now several branches of this family of large, thickset animals with trunks. All were descended from the original *Moeritherium* by way of *Paleomastodon,* but each now took its own evolutionary path.

One group was the mastodons, to whom we shall return shortly. They developed a novel method of replacing their grinding teeth. Most animals, including man, have several sets of teeth in a lifetime; the new teeth sprout under the old ones and rise vertically from the jaw until they push the old teeth out. Little *Moeritherium,* which had six pairs of grinding teeth, followed this arrangement. But the mastodons evolved a pattern of horizontal tooth replacement. New teeth began growing at the backs of their jaws, and moved toward the front of the mouth as the old teeth wore away. Eventually, when there was only a stub of the old tooth left, it was pushed out, not from below but from behind. Mastodons had two of these huge grinders on each side of each jaw, making eight altogether.

Another branch was that of the *dinotheres,* a name coined from the Greek words meaning "terrible beast." The dinotheres continued to replace their teeth vertically, like most other mammals. They stood about eight feet at the shoulders and had tusks only in their lower jaws; these were strange tusks that curved downward and backward toward the animal's chest. About twenty million years ago dinotheres were widely distributed through Africa and Asia, and at least one African form survived until perhaps a million years ago. One giant form from southeastern Europe, *Dinotherium gigantissimum,* stood close to thirteen feet high, on a par with the biggest elephants of modern times.

The third branch of trunk-bearing animals seems to have been an offshoot from the mastodon line. Like the mastodons, these animals replaced their grinding teeth horizontally, pushing them out from behind. But mastodon teeth had high knobby crests with deep valleys between them; in this other line, the valleys became filled with a cement-like substance, until the crests were mere low ridges sticking up from a flat surface. The number of crests increased, also, so that there might be fourteen to thirty ridges, instead of the six or eight of mastodons. There were two tusks as well, sprouting from the upper jaw.

The earliest form of this creature is called *Stego-lophodon*—a name that describes the special features of its teeth. Five or eight million years later there emerged a form called *Stegodon*, with more crests and lower ridges. From these evolved animals that had a single huge, flat grinder on each side of each jaw, making four in all. These were the true elephants.

The world was warm and elephants spread to nearly every part of it, and in widely separated places evolution took somewhat different paths. Three distinct families of elephants evolved: Asian elephants, African elephants, and mammoths.

The first members of the mammoth family, as we have said, evolved some two million years ago. Their curved tusks, many-ridged grinders, and massive skeletons are their identifying characteristics. These early mammoths, which lived before the first of the four ice ages, are generally classed in the genus *Archidiskodon*, again a name referring to certain aspects of their teeth. *Archidiskodon planifrons*, the flat-browed mammoth, seems to have been the oldest representative of this group. It was succeeded by *Archidiskodon meridionalis*, the southern mammoth, which also lived in southern Europe before the ice came. The American member of the group in those pre-ice-age days was *Archidiskodon imperator*, the imperial mammoth.

All of the *Archidiskodons* were truly mammoth mammoths, standing twelve to fourteen feet tall. The gigantic imperial mammoth of the United States may have been the bulkiest land mammal that ever existed; it was not only tall but big in every di-

Ancestors of the elephant, after reconstructions by
Maurice Wilson. above: the shovel-tusker, Platybelodon grangeri
below: Trilophodon angustidens

above : Moeritherium and Phiomia in a swamp
below : Palaeoloxodon antiquus, the straight-tusked elephant

mension, and may have attained weights of close to twenty tons. (The heaviest known modern elephant weighed twelve tons.) Skeletons of this huge mammoth may be seen in many American museums. A particularly rich supply of *Archidiskodon imperator* fossils was discovered near Los Angeles in the nineteenth century, at the La Brea tar pits, where prehistoric animals of many kinds were trapped in sticky asphalt deposits.

The imperial mammoth may have survived in the New World until eight or ten thousand years ago, according to certain archaeological evidence that is still open to dispute; but the other members of the genus *Archidiskodon* vanished much earlier. These were mammoths that required a tropical climate, and as the first ice age began they were forced to give way.

Evolution produced new elephant forms, probably descended from *Archidiskodon,* that were able to withstand a somewhat colder environment. Scientists usually class these temperate-climate mammoths in the genus *Parelephas.* This genus seems to have brought forth the biggest mammoth of all, a German form known as *Parelephas trogontherii.* This creature of the first and second ice ages exceeded 14 feet in height, and one specimen stood at least 14 feet 9 inches tall at the shoulders. It lived in a world that was gradually getting colder, and was able to adapt to the changing conditions. *Archidiskodon* had needed lush forest vegetation as its food supply, but *Parelephas* was a grazing animal capable of surviving on the open, grassy plains that were replacing Europe's forest in the cold weather. Probably it was a hairy animal—the forerunner of the woolly mammoth.

The North American representative of this type was *Parelephas columbi*, the Columbian mammoth. Most of the mammoth skeletons on display in American museums belong to this species; there is a particularly fine one at the American Museum of Natural History in New York. The Columbian mammoth had unusually long tusks, which tended to cross at the tips when the animal grew old.

By the end of the first ice age, *Parelephas* was so well adapted to cold weather that it migrated north to avoid the returning warmth. It had become a true northern animal. It was replaced in Europe by a huge straight-tusked elephant, *Paleoloxodon antiquus*, which had originated in Africa. This was a forest-dwelling animal of great height—sometimes close to fifteen feet tall—that lived in Mediterranean Europe and spread north as climate permitted. It is thought to be the ancestor of the modern African elephant.

An odd form that appeared during this warm interglacial period was the dwarf elephant, *Paleoloxodon falconeri*. Though elephant-like in every respect, this animal stood no more than three feet high when fully grown. Its fossil remains have been found on the island of Malta; similar species lived on other Mediterranean islands such as Cyprus and Crete. There was also an American dwarf elephant whose remains have been unearthed on islands off the coast of California.

The second ice age brought *Parelephas trogon-therii* down from the north into central Europe, and sent the straight-tusked *Paleoloxodon antiquus* on a migration into warmer lands. However, this big forest elephant was able to return to Europe in the warm years between the second and third ice ages.

But when the glaciers came to Europe for the third time, several hundred thousand years ago, they brought with them a new type of mammoth: *Mammuthus primigenius,* the woolly mammoth. The processes of evolution had developed this shaggy animal out of *Parelephas trogontherii,* it seems, creating an elephant even better able to survive ice-age conditions. In the third ice age and again in the fourth, the woolly mammoth spread through Europe, Asia, and across from Siberia into the New World. In the warm period between these ice ages, the mammoths retreated and more southerly elephant species expanded their range.

In the United States, the woolly mammoth seems to have replaced the Columbian mammoth as the main cold-weather species, just as it replaced *trogontherii* in Europe. But the Columbian mammoth apparently held its own in the middle latitudes of the United States even after the woolly species evolved; and the ancient form *Archidiskodon impe-rator* may have lingered in California and the Southwest, so that three types of mammoths inhabited the United States simultaneously from 250,000 to 10,000 years ago.

Since the United States also had a considerable population of mastodons at that time, it may have been the world's greatest living museum of elephant-like creatures. The mastodons, as we have already seen, belonged to the main line of evolution of these trunked animals. When the ancestors of the elephants and mammoths split away from that line more than twenty million years ago by evolving a different kind of grinding teeth, mastodons did not follow. The mastodons never evolved the flat ridged teeth that distinguish elephants and mammoths from the rest of the trunked tribe, although otherwise they came to look very much like true elephants.

While the elephant line was evolving through such early forms as *Stegodon* and *Archidiskodon* toward the woolly mammoth and the forest elephant, the mastodons were going through their own complicated evolutionary changes. Henry Fairfield Osborn, an American paleontologist of the early twentieth century who spent most of his long life studying fossil elephants and mastodons, was able to identify four families and 15 subfamilies of mastodons, and probably there were many other types whose fossil remains have not come down to us.

Some of the early mastodons had four tusks, two in the upper jaw curving down, two in the lower jaw slanting up. In two of the subfamilies the upper and lower tusks crossed like the blades of scissors, which must have been useful in ripping up plants for food. Another group of mastodons had small upper tusks, or none at all, but huge shovel-shaped lower ones.

These strange-looking animals died out millions of years ago. The mastodons of more recent times had

Comparison of mastodon and mammoth

Mastodon and skull

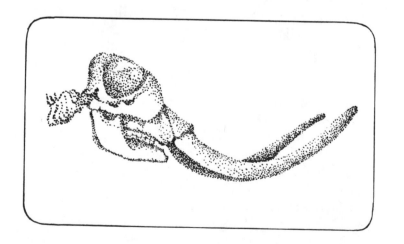

Woolly mammoth and skull

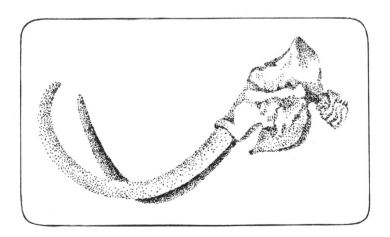

a closer resemblance to elephants, though there were some important differences in the shape of the tusks as well as in the grinding teeth. Some had tusks that curved gently upward as in elephants, but one species had tusks that curved downward, and another had tusks hooking sharply upward. *Cordillerion,* a small mastodon that inhabited ancient Arizona, California, Mexico, and Central and South America, had tusks that were twisted corkscrew-fashion. *Anancus,* a European mastodon that lived before the first ice age, was armed with a pair of enormous straight tusks nearly two thirds as long as its body.

Mastodons once were found in much of Europe and Asia. They also spread into the New World by crossing from Siberia to Alaska; several million years ago a bridge of land connected those two regions, which today are separated by the water of the Bering Strait. But the Old World mastodons all became extinct at the onset of the glacial era; there were no mastodons in Europe at the time when the woolly mammoth flourished. In the Americas, though, the species known as *Mastodon americanus* survived the coming of the ice and lasted until quite recent times, dying out less than 10,000 years ago.

This was the animal whose bones were found so profusely at Big Bone Lick—the most familiar of the mastodons, the beast Thomas Jefferson insisted on calling a "mammoth." The American mastodon was quite elephant-like: a stocky animal nine or ten feet tall with a thick trunk, large upward-curving tusks, a heavy rounded body, and a long sloping forehead. Judging from remains found in swamps in the eastern United States, it was covered with coarse golden-brown hair, though it was not as shaggy as the woolly mammoth.

About 25,000 years ago a worldwide catastrophe began to overtake the mastodons, the mammoths, and others of their kind. The fourth ice age had passed its peak, and the world was gradually thawing, until, thousands of years later, it reached something close to its present climate. During that period of climatic upheavals the big land mammals were pushed toward the brink of extinction.

The European forest elephant, *Palcoloxodon antiquus*, had died out at the beginning of the fourth ice age. Mammoths of the *Archidiskodon* and *Parelephas* groups were gone entirely by then also, except in a few parts of the United States. Now, as Europe warmed, the woolly mammoths were forced to take refuge in Siberia, and the mammoths and mastodons of North America found life growing equally difficult in their familiar range. Eventually, as we know, all cold-weather and temperate-zone mastodons and mammoths perished. The only animals of the entire family that survived were tropical ones, the elephants of Africa and Asia.

Two scientific questions emerge from this mass extinction: why did the mastodons and mammoths vanish from the earth, and when did the last ones die?

No one so far has offered a completely acceptable explanation for the great extinction. As recently as 1887, it was still possible for a serious scholar, Sir Henry Howorth, to produce a book arguing that a

sudden cataclysm had wiped the big animals out. He
wrote:

"These facts . . . prove in the first place that a
great catastrophe or cataclysm occurred at the close
of the Mammoth period, by which that animal, with
its companions, were overwhelmed over a very large
part of the earth's surface. Secondly, this cataclysm
involved a very wide-spread flood of water, which
not only killed the animals but also buried them
under continuous beds of loam or gravel. Thirdly,
that the same catastrophe was accompanied by a
very great and sudden change of climate in Siberia,
by which the animals which had previously lived in
fairly temperate conditions were frozen in their
flesh underground and have remained frozen ever
since."

However, careful geological research has produced no evidence at all that a global flood of this
sort ever occurred, nor was there any "very great
and sudden change of climate" from warm to cold in
Siberia. Changes of climate do not happen suddenly.
An even bigger objection to the sudden-catastrophe
theory is the fact that if there was a flood, it must
have been a highly selective one. It wiped out mammoths and mastodons, and such other big mammals
as the woolly rhinoceros, the giant ground sloth, the
giant bison, the saber-toothed tiger, and the giant
dire wolf. But many other animals that were contemporaries of those remained as numerous as ever:
deer, antelope, moose, fox, beaver, and so on. Certainly the mammoths, mastodons, and other bulky
beasts were the victims of a catastrophe, but it was

not the violent and instant catastrophe in which Howorth believed; it was a slow, private downfall involving only certain species and coming about over thousands of years.

It has often been suggested that the change in the world's climate at the end of the fourth ice age caused the extinctions. The period when the big mammals were disappearing—from 20,000 to 6,000 years ago, mainly—certainly coincided with a period of great climatic shifts. As the glaciers dwindled, tundra regions became forest land. To the south, where there had been no glaciers, rainfall patterns changed, so that cool, wet country became hot and dry, and deserts replaced forests. But these changes did not occur with drastic swiftness. There was ample time for the cold-weather animals to migrate to the regions that now offered the climate they preferred. All of the species that vanished as the world grew warm had endured equally great changes of climate in the past; the woolly mammoth had survived the end of the third ice age by heading north, so why should the end of the fourth ice age have seen its extinction?

And also, once again, why would some species perish as the climate changed, and others live on as if nothing had happened? Why did the dire wolf die, but not the timber wolf? Why did the giant bison disappear completely, while the bison of the American prairies thrived by the millions? Why did the prehistoric short-faced bear go, and the grizzly bear remain? The woolly mammoth and woolly rhinoceros departed, but such other ice-age animals as wolverines, Arctic foxes, reindeer, and musk oxen did not. Climatic shifts alone cannot explain such things.

Some zoologists have suggested that the big mammals became extinct simply because their time was up. That is, whole species, just like individuals, go through stages of youth, maturity, and old age, followed by death. The cycle may be relatively swift, passing from evolution to extinction in a million years or less; or it may be incredibly slow, taking hundreds of millions of years. But evidently it happens to all creatures. No matter how vigorous a species is, no matter how numerous, it eventually comes to the downhill side of its curve of development, and slopes toward extinction.

Those who follow this theory point to the fact that the mammoths of each ice age apparently were smaller than those of the ice age before. *Parelephas trogontherii* of the second ice age reached heights of fourteen feet or more. When *Mammuthus primigenius,* the woolly mammoth, appeared in the third ice age, it stood ten to twelve feet tall. In the beginning of the fourth ice age, the same species averaged nine to ten feet for males, eight to nine feet for females; and the mammoths that existed 10,000 to 15,000 years ago, at the close of that ice age, were even smaller. This dwindling in size, it is claimed, indicates a loss of vitality in the species. As the centuries passed and mammoths grew smaller, they became weaker, less able to withstand disease, changes in their environment, and natural enemies, until at last a time came when deaths outnumbered births and the species was doomed.

Perhaps so. But this theory only evades the real question. It does not tell us *why* extinction came to the mammoth and the mastodon. It only tells us that these animals became extinct because they had become vulnerable to extinction, which is not a very satisfactory explanation.

Many other theories have been proposed: an epidemic, a fatal burst of energy from an exploding star, chemical changes in the makeup of the ocean's supply of minerals, and so on. Most of these are ingenious but unconvincing. Even less likely is the idea, once taken quite seriously, that these species died out through a series of accidents. It was suggested that the mammoths, as they followed the retreating glaciers northward, tumbled one by one into hidden crevasses or became mired in muddy plains, until every last member of the species died. But the notion that every mammoth in the world perished after the fashion of the Beresovka mammoth is hard to accept.

The remaining possibility is that the downfall of the big mammals was the work of a new and deadly enemy: man. The period of the great extinctions coincided with a sudden upsurge in the size of the human population. Man had always been a rare species in prehistoric times. There may have been no more people in all of Europe during the fourth ice age than there are in one medium-sized town today, and the New World apparently did not have any human population at all until about 30,000 years ago. But as the world warmed, man's numbers increased greatly. He also became more skillful in the

A fallen mammoth

use of fire as a weapon, and designed more effective spears and darts. And, the theory goes, he began to make deep inroads on the animals about them, forcing some into extinction.

Plenty of evidence exists that the men of 20,000 years ago were active hunters. The charred bones of mammoths and bison are found in many sites. The ancient huntsmen stampeded whole herds by waving blazing torches, or even set forests afire to drive the panicky animals into traps. Undoubtedly these fire drives took a heavy toll of animal life, though it is not easy to see why such tactics should have exterminated the mammoth and mastodon while allowing the antelope and bison to survive.

When hunting parties closed in on a herd, they probably aimed their spears chiefly at young animals, since attacking full-grown ones would have been too dangerous. This must have had a particularly severe effect on the mammoth and mastodon population. All elephants have a slow rate of reproduction; a female elephant carries each unborn calf for nearly two years, and has only four or five offspring in her long lifetime. Such a constant cutting-out of the young members of the herd would reduce it, in time, to a collection of tough oldsters past the age of reproduction. Animals that bear young every year would not suffer as greatly from this as would mammoths or mastodons.

Yet hunting alone cannot account for the disappearance of these animals. There were not enough humans to exterminate whole species; so few people simply cannot have needed that much meat. And the

mammoth perished *everywhere,* even in remote
northern regions that had scarcely any human
beings. Also, the wave of extinction swept away a
good many animals that man did not hunt—the dire
wolf, the short-faced bear, a type of toad, a group of
snails—while it left some of the chief targets of his
spears, such as the prairie bison and the antelope.
And one wonders why so many species were exterminated in Europe, Asia, and the Americas, when
similar animals succeeded in continuing to flourish
down to our own day in Africa. Africa, too, had
skilled hunters.

The reason for the great extinction must lie in a
combination of factors. The change of climate was
one: when the world warmed some 20,000 years ago,
many of the ice-age mammals found their zone of
habitation growing smaller. The inner decline of
species may have been another: mammoths and mastodons may have been on evolution's downward
slope. The spread of the human population was a
third factor. It is probably not correct to say that
the hunters exterminated the big animals, but they
may very well have sped the process of extinction,
cutting down herds that already were being thinned
by natural causes.

Very likely these and other factors, coinciding, operated to wipe out the big game at the close of the
fourth ice age. Only in Africa, where climatic
changes had been relatively minor, did elephants
and rhinos and the other great beasts survive. At this
point we must say, however, that we have no solid
understanding of the reasons why so many long-es-

tablished species of important animals vanished in such a short span of time.

We know from archaeological evidence that the mammoth must have disappeared from Europe about 15,000 years ago. It is possible to assign dates fairly confidently to the sequence of human cultures in prehistoric Europe, and the archaeological record shows that after that time men ceased to paint pictures of mammoths, or to use mammoth bone and ivory for weapons and tools. Thick new forests of birch, willow, and pine had replaced the barren tundra and swampy taiga in Europe. These thickets were no place for bulky beasts like the woolly mammoth, and they set out for the north, for the cold open grasslands they preferred.

But the woolly beasts survived in northern Siberia long after they had departed from Europe. The same process of warming that made Europe uncomfortable for them created new grazing lands in the far north. During the ice age, Siberia had been buried under thick glaciers; not even mammoths could live there then. Now, in the time of thaw, taiga and tundra emerged in the north. The Siberian climate 10,000 years ago must have been much as it is today. Recent Russian research has demonstrated that the same tundra plants—wild thyme, crowsfoot, Alpine poppy, grasses, and sedges—grew in Siberia in the days of the mammoths as at present.

If the Siberian climate has been ideal for mammoths for the past 10,000 years, and there were relatively few hunters in Siberia, why did the mammoth eventually become extinct even there? We simply do not know. We can only fall back on the explanation that explains nothing: that the mammoth died out because its time on earth was over.

It is quite possible that a few mammoths still roamed Siberia a thousand years ago, or even more recently. The Siberian taiga is the largest forest in the world, covering nearly 3 million square miles— about three-fourths the area of the United States. Much of it is inhabited only by small bands of semi-nomadic hunters. Parts of the taiga may never have been explored. There is ample room for herds of mammoths to have lingered, unnoticed, well into historic times.

Stories of such survivors have occasionally come to light. In 1581, for example, Russian merchants sent a band of Cossack warriors into Siberia to bring unruly natives into line. This was the beginning of the Russian conquest of Siberia. Ermak Timofeyevich, the Cossack leader, reported that one of the first things he and his men saw east of the Ural Mountains was "a large hairy elephant." The natives told him that it was a valuable food animal which they called by a name meaning "mountain of meat." This was a century before anyone in Russia had heard of the mysterious Siberian *mammut,* and two centuries before it was realized that the *mammut* was not a giant underground rat, but in fact a hairy elephant.

A similar tale emerged in the twentieth century. In 1920 a French diplomat named Gallon, stationed in Siberia, met a Russian hunter who had just spent four years exploring the taiga. The hunter told Gallon how, in his second year in the forest, he came

upon "a huge footprint pressed deep into the mud.
It must have been about two feet across the widest
part and about eighteen inches the other way, that's
to say the spoor wasn't round but oval. There were
four tracks, the tracks of four feet, the first two
about twelve feet from the second pair, which were a
little bigger in size. Then the track suddenly turned
east and went into the forest of middling-sized elms.
Where it went in I saw a huge heap of dung; I had a
good look at it and saw it was made up of vegetable
matter. Some ten feet up, just where the animal had
gone into the forest, I saw a sort of row of broken
branches, made, I don't doubt, by the monster's
enormous head as it forced its way into the place
where it had decided to go. . . ."

The hunter followed the track eastward for days.
One day he saw another track, just like the first; two
of the huge animals had met and now were marching
together. He went on, somewhat nervously, until he
succeeded in getting near the giant beasts:

"The wind was in my face, which was good for
approaching them without them knowing I was
there. All of a sudden I saw one of the animals quite
clearly, and now I must admit I really was afraid. It
had stopped among some young saplings. It was a
huge elephant with big white tusks, very curved; it
was a dark chestnut color as far as I could see. It
had fairly long hair on the hind-quarters, but it
seemed shorter on the front. I must say I had no
idea that there were such big elephants. . . . The
second beast was around; I saw it only a few times
among the trees. It seemed to be the same size."

He did not have the sort of ammunition one

should use in shooting elephants, and the weather was growing too cold for him to continue tracking them. He left the animals in the forest and returned to his winter shelter. When questioned by the French diplomat, the hunter said that he had seen elephants only in pictures. "Such," Gallon wrote, "was the tale of this man who was too ignorant to know that what he had actually seen were mammoths. And when I told him the name, he did not show the least sign that he understood what I meant."

Do mammoths still exist in Siberia? Perhaps they do—although no modern hunter has ever returned with a fresh mammoth carcass, no explorer has ever taken a photograph of a live mammoth, and no scientific expedition has ever found the remains of a mammoth less than many thousands of years old. The possibility that Siberian mammoths survive today is an exciting one, but it seems rather slim.

North America is another place where mammoths were able to live on long after they had vanished from Europe. Mastodons, too, which had been extinct in Europe for more than a million years, could be found in the United States until just a few thousand years ago. And many Indian tribes had legends of such animals in the time of their forefathers. It was quite reasonable for Thomas Jefferson to hope that the Lewis and Clark expedition would discover some live mammoths in the continent's unknown interior.

Of course, Lewis and Clark saw no mammoths, and we know today that the only living elephants in the United States are those in circuses and zoos. Mammoths and mastodons have probably been extinct in the Americas for thousands of years. Some archaeologists once believed that they became extinct there before the first human beings arrived in the New World. We know now that that is not so; the ancestors of the Indians did indeed live here when mammoths and mastodons existed, and hunted the big animals. But the scientific controversy over that issue deserves a chapter of its own.

CHAPTER EIGHT

AMERICA'S ANCIENT MASTODON HUNTERS

The nature of the scientific process involves a good deal of debate. One scholar puts forth a theory; another, skeptical, challenges it; the discussion that follows outlines the areas of disagreement, exposes faulty conclusions, and—perhaps—yields a new morsel of firm knowledge. If scientific debates often seem to generate more heat than light, it is because scientists, like ordinary mortals, are capable of defending a favorite opinion even in the face of common sense.

One of the most violent archaeological disputes of the late nineteenth and early twentieth centuries had to do with the date of the arrival of mankind in the New World. One faction of scientists believed that human beings had lived in the Americas only for the past two or three thousand years. The other side argued that the first men had reached the New World a good deal before that—anywhere from 10,-000 to 50,000 years ago. The solution of the disagreement turned on knowing whether such ice-age beasts as the mammoth and the mastodon had still existed in the New World when the first men arrived.

Both sides agreed that man had come to the Western Hemisphere very late in his evolutionary career. Since the discovery of the first Neanderthal skull in the middle of the nineteenth century, it was generally recognized that man had passed through a series of evolutionary stages on the route to his modern appearance. Several earlier human forms had existed, thickboned, chinless, with bulging brows and sloping foreheads. The earliest of these had evolved more than a million years ago, in Africa or Asia.

But while fossil human remains of many strange, primitive types were found in many parts of the Old World in the nineteenth century, none were discovered in the Americas. Nor did the New World hold any apes, fossil or otherwise; gorillas, chimpanzees, orang-utans, and other close relatives of man were unknown outside the Old World. It was a fair conclusion, then, that the story of human evolution had taken place overseas. When man got to the Western Hemisphere he had already evolved to something close to his modern form.

There was also no serious quarrel over the route he had taken. The only place where the New World can easily be reached from the Old is the Bering Strait, today a 56-mile-wide stretch of shallow water

separating Alaska from Siberia. It is hard to imag-
ine primitive man coming to the New World across
the Atlantic or Pacific, but easy to see how, even
with his extremely limited skills, he could have
crossed the Bering Strait. The strait is broken by
two islands, the Diomedes, so that the longest
stretch of open water is only 23 miles. Men paddling
the clumsiest of canoes should have been able to
manage that. And in winter Bering Strait freezes
over. A bridge of ice is formed, over which men can
—and do—cross from Asia to North America.

If the first men entered Alaska during the last ice
age, they would not have had to bother building canoes or hiking over ice. They could have walked
across the Bering Strait on dry land. So much water
was locked up in glaciers during the ice age that sea
levels were more than 250 feet lower than they are
today. The continental shelf of eastern North America was above water, so that mastodons and other
animals grazed in places now forty miles out to sea.
And the Bering Strait, which at its deepest point is
only 180 feet deep, held no water.

By Thomas Jefferson's time it was generally as-
sumed that the ancestors of the American Indians
had drifted out of Asia across the strait in a series
of gradual migrations, fanning out over the Americas over the course of many years.

But how long ago did the migrations begin?

In providing an answer to that question, nineteenth-century American archaeologists had to take
into account the curious myth of the Mound Builders. Many regions of the United States, early ex-

plorers had discovered, contained puzzling earthen mounds. Some were of colossal size, like the Cahokia Mound in Illinois, 100 feet high and covering 16 acres. Others were small rounded hills of a clearly artificial nature. Associated with the mounds were walls and geometrical enclosures, also of earth and in some cases thousands of feet in length. The greatest concentration of these earthworks was in Ohio, Illinois, Indiana, and Missouri, but there was also a major mound area in the southeast, and hardly a state east of the Mississippi did not have at least some of these structures. Within most mounds were relics of past races: human bones, weapons, tools, jewelry.

The early American settlers could not believe that the Indians who lived in the mound regions at the time of their discovery had built them. Those Indians were simple wandering savages, hardly capable of the sustained effort needed to quarry tons of earth and shape it into a symmetrical mound. So people began to spin tales of the Mound Builders, a legendary race that had lived in North America *before* the Indians. These fantastic ancient people had had a lofty civilization, it was said, but eventually they had been destroyed, either in a civil war or through attack by marauding Indians, and the mounds were the only trace of their existence.

No one could say how long ago the Mound Builders had lived, but obviously it had been far in the past—five, ten, maybe fifty thousand years ago. They had existed, some people claimed, at a time so distant that such extinct prehistoric creatures as the mammoth, the mastodon, and the giant ground sloth still were found in the United States.

The proof that Mount Builders and mastodons had lived at the same time was extremely shaky. In the 1850's, farmers in Wisconsin discovered a mound that seemed to have the form of an elephant. It was 133 feet in length, with a trunk 31 feet long. Obviously the Mound Builders had used a mammoth or a mastodon as their model! A few skeptics did point out, though, that the animal had neither tusks nor a tail, and that its trunk was shorter than proper proportions demanded; perhaps the "trunk" was nothing more than soil accidentally piled up by flood waters, and the mound really depicted a bear, they said.

Then, in 1880, a clergyman from Davenport, Iowa, whose hobby was investigating mounds, excavated a group of them near his city and found a clay pipe that bore the image of an elephant. Animal pipes had been discovered in many mounds, depicting in lifelike manner such beasts as otters, beavers, ravens, and frogs; but no one had ever seen an elephant pipe before. It showed a bulky little animal that had no tusks but otherwise was a good likeness of an elephant. The same clergyman obtained a second elephant pipe from an Iowa farmer in 1882.

Aside from the Wisconsin elephant mound and the Iowa elephant pipes, there was nothing whatever to prove that the Mound Builders had lived in the era of mammoths and mastodons. The bones of many animals were found in mounds, but not the bones or tusks of these ancient behemoths. (This did not prevent one writer from suggesting in 1880 that the

Mound Builders probably had tamed and harnessed mammoths and used them in constructing their tremendous earthworks.) However, several earlier nineteenth-century fossil discoveries did seem to indicate that some prehistoric inhabitants of the United States—not necessarily Mound Builders—had definitely hunted mastodons and other animals now extinct.

The first of these finds was the work of "Dr." Albert Koch—the same man who pieced together the bones of several mastodons to create the marvelous horned monster he called *Missourium*. In October, 1838, two years before the *Missourium* exploit, Koch learned that a farmer in Gasconade County, Missouri, had uncovered some large animal bones five feet underground while digging a well. With the bones lay a stone knife and an Indian axe. Koch went to the farm and obtained permission to conduct further excavations. His report on what he found appeared, for some unknown reason, in a Philadelphia magazine called *The Presbyterian*. Its issue of January 12, 1839, bore an anonymous article headed, "The Mammoth," in which Koch declared:

It is with the greatest pleasure, the writer of this article can state, from personal knowledge, that one of the largest of these animals, has actually been stoned and buried by Indians, as appears from the implements found among the ashes, cinders, half burned wood, and bones of the animal. . . .

Koch described how he discovered a stone knife at the site, and then "a large quantity of pieces of rocks, weighing from two to twenty-five pounds each, evidently thrown there with the intention of hitting some object. . . ." Below that lay a spear and an axe, and then a layer of ashes, broken spears, axes, knives, and pieces of bone, six inches to a foot in depth. The remains of the "mammoth"—it was actually a mastodon—had been burned. Koch thought that the animal had become trapped in a muddy spring and had fallen on its right side; Indians had come upon the helpless beast, killed it, and roasted it on the spot.

Nothing like this had ever been found in the United States before. In Europe, in 1839, most people still doubted that human beings had been around to hunt "antediluvian" creatures such as mammoths; but here, from Missouri, came apparent proof that they had. Among those who found the article in *The Presbyterian* exciting was the great naturalist Benjamin Silliman of Yale, who called upon the unknown author to get in touch with him at once. But Koch evidently did not learn of Silliman's request, since he made no attempt to come forward. This is perhaps the best evidence that the Gasconade County find was authentic. If Koch were perpetrating a hoax, he would not have done it anonymously; there could be no glory in that.

He did not identify himself as the author of *The Presbyterian*'s article until the summer of 1841, when he was in Kentucky exhibiting his *Missourium* concoction. Then he issued a booklet describing his various fossil finds, and in it was a section headed, "Evidence of Human Existence Contemporary with Fossil Animals." It has been generally believed, Koch wrote, that mastodons and other antediluvian animals "existed and became extinct previous to the creation of the race of men; which supposition was founded on the fact that no evidence of human existence could be traced back to, or found with, those antediluvian animals." Koch believed, however, that the lack of such evidence reflected nothing more than careless examination of the archaeological record.

He went on to describe the discovery of the Gasconade County animal (which he now thought was a mastodon, not a mammoth) and the artifacts and traces of fire associated with it. He told how he found, "nine feet beneath the surface, a layer of ashes from six to twelve inches in thickness, mingled with charcoal, large pieces of wood partly burned, together with Indian implements of war, as stone arrowheads, tomahawks, &c., &c."

These were important discoveries. They showed that man had lived in the New World at a very early date, or else that mastodons had survived there until quite recently; either way, the implications were profound. But few scientists took Koch seriously. To them he was merely an archaeological profiteer, a sensation-monger, a publicity-seeker interested chiefly in dollars. Any man who would put a fossil together as he had done with *Missourium*, and then go on a circus-like tour exhibiting it, could hardly be worthy of respect or attention.

In this case, there was no reason to think Koch was working a hoax. There was no profit in it for him, and, since he published his first report on the charred mastodon anonymously, he did not even seem to want fame. Yet his findings were wholly discredited.

The *Missourium* affairs hardly helped his reputation. After he sold that skeleton in 1844, he quickly appeared with a new wonder: a gigantic 114-foot-long skeleton of a "sea serpent" he called *Hydrarchus*. It drew tremendous crowds in American exhibition halls until a famed zoologist named Jeffries Wyman pointed out that it was actually the fossil of an extinct whale, which Koch had decorated by adding bones from at least four other animals. Abashed, Koch hurried *Hydrarchus* off to England, but his reception was chilly there and he quickly left for Germany, where things went better. A German scientist pronounced *Hydrarchus* genuine and Koch sold it to the Royal Museum in Berlin at a fine price.

In later years, he settled in St. Louis and seems to have sought eagerly to win scientific respectability. Apparently it pained him to realize that he was regarded as a fraud by the men whose esteem he most dearly craved. In particular he tried to defend his claim of having found an association of human artifacts with the remains of fossil mammals. This, too, had been attacked; some scientists had said that the weapon points he had found had been carried into the sites by stream action long after the mastodons had died.

Koch replied to his critics, discussing the position

of the weapons relative to the bones and showing
how obvious it was that prehistoric men had killed
and roasted the mastodon. In the last years of his
life, until his death in 1866, Koch lived quietly, publishing nothing and harboring deep bitterness for
those who refused to accept his one genuine contribution to science. He had put horns on a mastodon,
he had doubled the length of a whale and called it a
fossil sea serpent, he had committed many a crime
against truth, yes—but he had also shown that man
in North America had hunted prehistoric behemoths, and it pained him that his fondness for fame
as a showman had robbed him of credit for that
scientific achievement.

By ill luck the discoverer of the other important
nineteenth-century find of this sort was also a showman more than a scientist. He was Montroville Wilson Dickeson, who dug for Mound Builder relics and
took them on tour. From 1837 to 1844, Dickeson
toured the United States with a painted panorama
on cloth, which was constantly enlarged to include
new discoveries. As it unrolled, it displayed fanciful
scenes of the most famous mounds. A handbill ad-
vertising this traveling show declared:

MONUMENTAL GRANDEUR OF THE
MISSISSIPPI VALLEY, with scientific
lectures on AMERICAN AERCHIOL-
OGY. . . . THIS GORGEOUS PAN-
ORAMA with all the ABORIGINAL MON-
UMENTS of a large extent of country once
roamed by the RED MAN, was painted by

the EMINENT ARTIST I. J. EGAN,
ESQ., and covers 15,000 feet of Canvas. . . .

In 1846, excavating near Natchez, Mississippi,
Dickeson found a human pelvic bone among the
bones of mastodon, giant ground sloth, and other extinct animals. The human bone was stained the same
dark color as the other fossils and was in the same
condition. Dickeson at once claimed to have demonstrated that the bone was of the same age as those
of the extinct animals. However, Dickeson's reputation was not one that inspired much faith in his
claims. Even though he insisted he had found the
human bone embedded in clay below the remains of
three giant ground sloths, one celebrated scientist of
the time—the geologist Charles Lyell—suggested
that it had come from a recent Indian grave and had
somehow been washed into a lower level by the
weather. The dark staining, Lyell said, came from
the peaty soil in which the bone could have been lying before it entered the clay.

The odd thing is that if Koch and Dickeson had
not been such disreputable individuals, their finds
would probably have been hailed as major discoveries. Most American scientists in the middle of the
nineteenth century were believers in the Mound
Builder myth, and thus saw nothing strange about
finding human bones or weapons mixed with the remains of mastodons. Only a few men were bold
enough to deny that this vanished race of Mound
Builders had ever existed. These men claimed that

the mounds had been built within the last five hundred or a thousand years by the ancestors of the present-day American Indians; but their voices went unheard. People preferred to believe in a glorious empire of ancient Mound Builders, and there was no reason why those ancient heroes could not have hunted mastodons.

By 1880—about the time the Iowa elephant pipes were coming to light—many of man's ideas about the past had begun to change. By then the old idea of an "antediluvian" world was on its way out; the concept of ice ages alternating with warmer eras had begun to develop. In Europe, where scientists had once tried to deny that man could have been a contemporary of the mammoth, ample proof was now at hand that he had been. It was becoming clear to European archaeologists that the story of man went well back into the supposed "antediluvian" period.

In the United States the opposite idea was emerging. Scientists there had previously been much too willing to believe fantastic theories of Mound Builders who lived twenty or fifty thousand years ago. Suddenly the pendulum swung the other way. The new archaeologists called the Mound Builder myth mere foolishness, and termed such things as the elephant pipes clever fakes. There had never been any grand prehistoric empires in the United States, they said. The Indians had been the first inhabitants of the New World, and they had come here only two or three thousand years ago at the earliest.

The center of such ideas was the Bureau of American Ethnology, a division of the Smithsonian Institution. Major John Wesley Powell, the head of the bureau, had long believed that the Mound Builders were just the ancestors of contemporary Indian tribes, and that at least some of them had still been building mounds and earthen ramparts when the first white explorers arrived. Powell sent teams of archaeologists into the field for a careful examination of the mounds. By 1895 there could be no doubt that Powell had been correct. The Mound Builder empire was a fantasy. A detailed survey of the mounds had shown that they were at most 1500 years old, while some contained such things as crucifixes and metal knives that could only have been acquired by the Indians after the coming of the white man to the New World.

When scientists puncture a popular fantasy, though, they sometimes go too far in their effort to destroy wild theories. Even if there had never been a Mound Builder civilization, it did not necessarily follow that there had been no human beings at all in the Americas thousands of years ago. But the same men who demolished the Mound Builder myth also insisted that the first Indians had come across the Bering Strait at about the time of Christ. It was folly to think otherwise, they said.

The main authority on these topics now was the Czech-born anthropologist Ales Hrdlicka, who in 1903 became the Smithsonian Institution's first curator of physical anthropology. Hrdlicka, a brilliant scientist and a devastating debater, systematically examined and confidently dismissed all evidence offered to show man's antiquity in the New World. He brushed aside the Koch and Dickeson discoveries by saying that the human relics had accidentally become mixed with those of the extinct animals. In the late nineteenth century, certain fossil human skulls had been found in the United States that were thought to be as old as the Neanderthal skulls of Europe; Hrdlicka spoke of them as "not in the least primitive," "essentially modern," "not to be distinguished from the modern Indian."

In this way he cleared away a great deal of error, confusion, and downright fraud. But he also put down some genuinely valuable finds. And as he grew older his opinions hardened into prejudices, which he proclaimed so vehemently that most scientists thought it would somehow be improper to hold an opposing belief. No one wanted to contradict fiery old Hrdlicka, for when anyone dared to suggest that men *had* lived in the United States in the time of the big extinct mammals, Hrdlicka immediately loosed a barrage of denunciation.

By the 1920's it seemed clear that the mammoth, mastodon, and other giant New World mammals had died out at least eight to ten thousand years ago. Hrdlicka himself accepted this. What he would not accept were such things as the Koch and Dickeson finds, which seemed to show that men had lived among those vanished beasts.

Then, in 1926, J.D. Figgins of the Denver Museum of Natural History, working near the town of Folsom, New Mexico, uncovered the skeleton of a long-extinct species of bison. A stone weapon point lay beside one of the bones. Surely this was proof enough that man had hunted the vanished ancient animals; but the experts scoffed, saying that the point was "intrusive" and had been carried to the level of the bison fossil by some burrowing rodent.

Figgins went back to Folsom in 1927. Once again he found a point—about two inches long, with a narrow groove down each face—associated with bison fossils. But this time the point lay *between the ribs* of the bison.

Halting work at once, Figgins sent telegrams to every important prehistorian in the country, inviting them to inspect the site before he proceeded with the excavation. Figgins was a fairly obscure archaeologist, and only three authorities responded; but fortunately they were highly respected. They supervised the dig and agreed that the 1927 Folsom point was indeed no intrusion. A human being, not a squirrel, had driven that point into the fossilized bison bone. And it had been done thousands of years ago.

Over three seasons, nineteen points were found at the site, as well as the skeletons of twenty-three bison. There was every reason to think that ancient American hunters had slain and consumed those bison. Significantly, the tail bones of each animal were missing, indicating that the huntsmen had skinned their prey. Since then, points of the Folsom type have been found all over North America—from Alaska to Georgia, in fact. No one now questions the fact that the makers of the Folsom points were hunters who wandered the North American continent thousands of years ago. Even Hrdlicka, before his

Hunter and mastodon

death in 1943, admitted that man must have entered
the Americas some 10,000 "or at most 15,000" years
ago.

In recent years weapon points of many kinds have
come to light that are known to be older than the
Folsom type, since they were found in levels below
those where Folsom points were found. Carbon-14
dating and other modern technical methods are helping to provide some idea of the age of these points.
The points themselves cannot be dated by carbon-14,
which works only with organic material; but bits of
charcoal found at one Folsom site gave a carbon-14
age of about 10,800 years. Among the pre-Folsom
sites, one in California produced a carbon-14 dating
of 30,000 years, and one in Texas a dating of more
than 38,000 years. These figures are controversial
and not all archaeologists accept their accuracy.
However, it is certain that the ancestors of the Indians were in the Americas 10,000 years ago, and quite
probable that they arrived fifteen thousand years before that.

It is also completely certain that some of these
early Americans were hunters of the mammoth and
the mastodon. Since 1932 the discovery of ancient
"kill sites" has become a fairly frequent if not exactly common event in American archaeology.

The 1932 find was made near Dent, Colorado,
when flood waters cut through a riverbank and exposed a great mass of large bones about 500 feet
south of the Union Pacific Railroad station. A railroad foreman notified Father Conrad Bilgery of
Regis College, Denver, who identified the bones as

those of mammoths. Father Bilgery and some of his archaeology students excavated and found a weapon point under one of the skeletons. It was something like a Folsom point, but larger and of cruder workmanship.

Father Bilgery invited the Denver Museum of Natural History to take over at the Dent site, and in 1933 a Museum expedition removed the bones of one large male mammoth and eleven young females. All of them were imperial mammoths, *Archidiskodon imperator*. The site yielded two more of the long, crude weapon points and a number of large stones that ancient hunters had apparently hurled at the mammoths. Although the carbon-14 method of dating had not yet been invented, geologists in the group estimated that the site was roughly as old as the Folsom site.

In 1932, archaeologists from the Philadelphia Academy of Sciences began to explore the dry beds of prehistoric lakes on a flat, parched plateau in New Mexico, near the Texas border. Bones and artifacts were unearthed in various places, and in 1934 John L. Cotter of the Academy excavated at a place called Blackwater Draw, near Clovis, New Mexico. Workmen had found a mammoth tooth and some thin stone tools while ploughing there the year before. Cotter discovered bison bones and Folsom points in the upper levels at Blackwater Draw; below were the remains of two mammoths, and four of the crude Dent-style grooved points. One lay an inch from a mammoth's spine and another was found between two leg bones. Cotter referred to these artifacts as Clovis points, and they are still called that today, though perhaps it would have been more accurate to name them Dent points. At Blackwater Draw, also, Cotter found stone knives and scrapers that might have been used for butchering mammoths, and two weapon points fashioned from mammoth bone.

The next discovery of this kind was made in 1951 near Naco, Arizona, close to the Mexican border. Two men from the area noticed mammoth bones and two Clovis points exposed on the side of a ravine, and sent word to the Arizona State Museum. The following year a team of archaeologists led by Emil W. Haury excavated the site. They found a mammoth skeleton and six more points; still another point was located farther up the ravine. Five of the points had struck the mammoth; one lay at the base of the skull, two were wedged between its ribs, one was in its left shoulderblade, and one had apparently killed it by severing its spine. The mammoth's hindquarters were missing, as though they had been carried away by the hunters.

Another kill site was detected in 1955 only a few miles from Naco, on the Lehner Ranch near Hereford, Arizona. Heavy rains had cut away the bank of a ravine there, laying bare fossil bones. Emil Haury of the Arizona State Museum excavated again, using power equipment to remove thousands of tons of earth. He uncovered the bones of nine young mammoths along with those of tapir, giant bison, and other extinct animals; and there were thirteen Clovis points in the site as well as eight

butchering tools. Charcoal from the Lehner site was
given a carbon 14 test and yielded an age of about
11,300 years.

Archaeologists now used carbon-14 to date the
other known kill sites. Dent yielded an age of about
11,200 years and Blackwater Draw an age of about
11,170 years. Two readings of material from the
Naco site produced a possible age of 9,250 years, but
some archaeologists suggested that an error had
been made in the calculations, since it was difficult to
believe that Naco was two thousand years more recent than Dent, Lehner, and Blackwater Draw.

Clovis points have been found in association with
mammoth bones at several other sites in the west.
One of the most recently discovered of these is Domebo, near Tonkawa, Oklahoma. As at most of the
other sites, erosion exposed mammoth bones along
the edge of a ravine. The fossil was discovered in
December, 1961, and excavation under the direction
of the Museum of the Great Plains, Lawton, Oklahoma, began the following March.

A gigantic imperial mammoth, thirteen to fourteen feet tall, had been killed at Domebo, or perhaps
had died of natural causes; the archaeologists were
uncertain about that, even though three Clovis
points were found with the skeleton. There was
some evidence that the mammoth had been cut apart
after its death. Later, fine sand covered the animal's
bones and a prehistoric flood buried the site in
clay.

Carbon-14 dating showed that the Domebo mammoth had died about 11,200 years ago. This is very

close to the dates obtained at the other Clovis-point kill sites, except for the doubtful Naco date. It appears that the Clovis people must have entered North America as a relatively small band about 12,-000 years ago; no Clovis site older than that has been found. They at once adopted mammoth-hunting as their specialty. Perhaps it was a specialty they had brought with them from Siberia, but we cannot be sure of that, since no Clovis points have ever been found there.

One expert on the Clovis people—C. Vance Haynes, director of the carbon-14 laboratory at the University of Arizona—thinks that they may have numbered no more than thirty individuals at first. He suggests that a single hunting band consisting of five or six families crossed the Bering Strait together. Within 500 years, Haynes calculates, the original thirty Clovis people would have increased to perhaps 12,500, making up about 400 widely scattered hunting bands. Thus they spread across the continent. Although all the Clovis mammoth kill sites found have been discovered west of the Mississippi, Clovis points and tools have been found at sites in such eastern states as Virginia, Pennsylvania, Alabama, and Tennessee. (A Clovis point was even found at Big Bone Lick in Kentucky in 1898, though no one then could identify it. It was not lying near mammoth or mastodon bones.)

The kill sites offer some idea of how the Clovis mammoth-hunters operated. At the Dent site, the mammoth bones were clustered at the mouth of a narrow gully below a sandstone cliff. Evidently the hunters had stampeded a herd of mammoths over the cliff. Perhaps some of the animals were killed by the fall; the rest, injured and unable to escape from the gully, were pelted with boulders and finished off with spear thrusts. (The Clovis points were probably mounted on wooden shafts. It is unlikely that they were arrowheads; the bow seems to have been a much later invention. Killing a mammoth with a stone point lashed to a shaft must have been a risky and difficult business.)

At Lehner, Domebo, and Blackwater Draw, the mammoths seem to have been taken by surprise as they were visiting streams. Possibly the hunters used a torchlit fire drive to frighten the animals into shallow water, where the rocky streambed would make their escape difficult. The nine Lehner mammoths were all quite young, as if the hunters had deliberately cut immature and less dangerous animals out of the herd.

Did the Clovis mammoth-hunters wipe out the mammoth? The archaeological record as it is known thus far seems to show that within five hundred or a thousand years after the emergence of the Clovis people, there were no mammoths left to hunt in the United States.

All of the Clovis sites have been dated within an extremely narrow range. The oldest is a little less than 12,000 years old. The most recent—aside from the disputed date of the Naco site—is slightly more than 11,000 years old. Then there is a short gap in the record, and the Folsom sites begin, at about 10,-800 years ago. Folsom was definitely slightly later than Clovis; this is shown not only by carbon-14 dating but by the fact that Folsom points lie above Clovis points whenever they are found in the same area. The makers of the Folsom points seem to have inhabited the United States from about 11,000 to 9,500 years ago.

No Folsom point has ever been found associated with a mammoth kill, nor have mammoth bones ever been found at a site marked by typical Folsom artifacts. The chief target of the Folsom hunters was the giant bison, now extinct. Bones of this bison are found at almost all Folsom sites. The Clovis people also hunted bison occasionally, but their preferred form of big game was the mammoth. Could it be that by the time the Folsom people appeared, the mammoths were gone?

It is unlikely that a mere ten or twelve thousand Clovis hunters, spread out over a vast continent, could have exterminated the American mammoths altogether within a few hundred years. But if the mammoth had already been in decline for natural reasons, the sudden entry of the Clovis people might well have helped to push it much closer to extinction. Even though time has destroyed most of the archaeological record, we have already been able to find traces of several dozen mammoths killed by Clovis hunters; it is quite possible that their total kills, over eight or nine hundred years, amounted to thousands of mammoths. This may have been a substantial portion of the entire mammoth population. The Clovis people may have thinned the mammoth herds so severely that the Folsom folk saw the big animals only on rare occasions. On the other hand, the Clovis kills may have been insignificant; possibly the major factor in driving the mammoth out of the western United States about 11,000 years ago was the shift from a cool, wet climate to a hot, dry one, which took place during the era of the Clovis people.

Apparently after the mammoth vanished from the western half of the country it was still hunted in the east, and so was the mastodon, which had always been more numerous in the eastern forests than on the western plains. But it is difficult to trace the development of these big-game-hunting cultures in the eastern United States. The west, with its dry climate and sparse population, is better suited for preserving early archaeological sites than the east, where the spread of civilization has destroyed many of ancient man's camping grounds.

Only one mastodon kill site—where bones and weapons are found close together—has been found in the eastern half of the country. This is the site in Gasconade County, Missouri, that "Dr." Albert Koch excavated in 1838. Koch sold the charred bones he had discovered to the museum of the University of Berlin; modern archaeologists, examining the controversial find, have confirmed that the bones were indeed that of a mastodon. The weapons associated with the skeleton resembled those known to have been used five to six thousand years ago. No carbon-14 dating has yet been done on the Gasconade County mastodon, but it may prove to be one of the most recent of all the ancient kill sites.

Other clues to the length of time the mammoth and mastodon survived in the New World are spotty. No reliable mammoth date more recent than 11,000 years ago has been reported. Fragments of a mastodon tusk found in Washtenaw County, Michigan, produced carbon-14 results indicating an age of 6,000 to 6,500 years. A mastodon skeleton discovered near Cromwell, Indiana, yielded a date of 5,300 years, but a recheck of that specimen gave an age nearly twice as great. Two weapon points lay about twenty feet from this skeleton.

It is quite possible that mastodons or mammoths continued to range certain parts of the United States until five or six thousand years ago. Maybe a few mastodons managed to hold their own much later than that—perhaps two or three thousand years ago—but no scientific evidence of that is available now. Despite the Indian legends of giant shaggy beasts in the northern forests, despite all rumors and hopeful reports, we are forced to say now that it has been thousands of years since elephants and their cousins, the mastodons, lived wild in the United States.

We are also unable to say with any firmness how long ago man first began hunting such animals in the New World. The Clovis people of 12,000 years ago are the earliest mammoth-hunters of whose date we can be confident.

There are several American sites whose carbon-14 dates are much older than Clovis, but none of these dates have won full acceptance yet from archaeologists. Charcoal samples from an ancient site at Lew-

isville, in northeastern Texas, were dated at more
than 38,000 years; the bones of mammoth, camel,
giant bison, giant land tortoise, and other extinct
American animals were found there, along with
three crude stone tools. But before archaeologists
examined this site, construction workers using
heavy earth-moving equipment had disturbed it, and
it has been argued that this may have created a mis-
leading jumble of sequences. Possibly the animal remains were forced into a much lower and older layer
containing the charcoal, which could have been
formed by fires started by natural causes. The presence of a Clovis point in the site supports this idea
of a mixing of levels, since it is most unlikely that
such weapons were being manufactured 38,000 years
ago.

On Santa Rosa Island off the California coast, the
remains of dwarf mammoths have been found, their
bones separated and charred as though they had
been butchered for a prehistoric barbecue. The car-
bon-14 age for these bones—again disputed—is
about 30,000 years.

In the spring of 1959, Dr. Juan Armenta Ca-
macho, working at a site southeast of Puebla, Mexico, found four fragments of mammoth or mastodon
bone on which can be seen the outlines of mammoths, snakes, camels, bison, and other animals—all
engraved when the bone was fresh. Some years later
the National Science Foundation and the American
Philosophical Society sponsored excavations at this
site under the general direction of Dr. J. O. Brew of
Harvard University. This work located crude stone

points and scraping blades, mixed with the remains
of mastodon, mammoth, dire wolf, and extinct species of antelope, horse, and camel. In the spring of
1967 the U.S. Geological Survey announced a car-
bon-14 age of more than 40,000 years for pieces of
charcoal found near the Puebla site. Tests at another laboratory showed an age only half as great;
but in either case this seems the oldest definite scene
of an encounter between men and mammoths in the
New World.

The story of the mammoths and the mastodons is
still unfolding on many fronts. There is much that
remains to be learned. We do not yet know why or
when these animals became extinct. We do not know
why the elephants of the tropics were able to survive while those of cooler climates perished. There
still are gaps in our understanding of the pattern of
evolution of the whole elephant family.

But, nevertheless, the amount of information we
have been able to recover since Thomas Jefferson's
day has been immense. An entire splendid chapter
of the world's ancient past has come to light. It is
fascinating for its own sake to know that mighty elephants once thundered through the forests of New
York and California, but our rediscovery of these
vanished titans is only one part of a much larger rediscovery. Since the days when men spoke of
''giants' bones,'' we have learned about the ice ages
and the other great climatic shifts, about the slow
climb of prehistoric man toward civilization, about
the existence of such once-unfamiliar concepts as

evolution and extinction. We see a panorama of the past, now, that our great-great-grandfathers could not have viewed. We see strange animals emerge, dominate, disappear. We know now that all things change except change itself.

BIBLIOGRAPHY

Armstrong, Terence. *The Russians in the Arctic*. London, Methuen, 1958.

Augusta, Josef. *A Book of Mammoths*. London, Paul Hamlyn, 1962.

Bakeless, John. *The Eyes of Discovery: America as Seen by the First Explorers*. New York, Dover, 1961.

Bibby, Geoffrey. *The Testimony of the Spade*. New York, Knopf, 1956.

Brebner, John Bartlet. *The Explorers of North America, 1492–1806*. London, A. & C. Black, 1955.

Carrington, Richard. *Mermaids and Mastodons*. London, Chatto & Windus, 1957.

Conger, Dean. "Siberia: Russia's Frozen Frontier." *National Geographic Magazine*, March, 1967.

De Camp, L. Sprague. *Elephant*. New York, Pyramid Books, 1964.

Dyson, James L. *The World of Ice*. New York, Knopf, 1962.

Giedion, Sigfried. *Eternal Present*. Vol. I: *The Beginnings of Art*. Princeton, Princeton University Press, 1964.

Haynes, C. Vance, Jr. "Elephant-Hunting in North America." *Scientific American*, June, 1966.

Heuvelmans, Bernard. *On the Track of Unknown Animals*. New York, Hill and Wang, 1959.

Howorth, H. H. *The Mammoth and the Flood*. London, Sampson Low, 1887.

Irwin, Cynthia and Henry, and Agogino, George. "Ice Age Man vs. Mammoth in Wyoming." *National Geographic Magazine*, June, 1962.

Jackson, Donald, ed. *Letters of the Lewis and Clark Expedition . . . 1783–1854*. Urbana, University of Illinois Press, 1962.

Jefferson, Thomas. *Notes on the State of Virginia*. Chapel Hill, University of North Carolina Press, 1955.

Leonhardy, Frank C., ed. *Domebo: A Paleo-Indian Mammoth Kill in the Prairie-Plains*. Lawton, Okla. Museum of the Great Plains, 1966.

Leroi-Gourhan, André. *Treasures of Prehistoric Art*. New York, Harry N. Abrams, 1967.

Ley, Willy. *Dawn of Zoology*. Englewood Cliffs, N.J., Prentice-Hall, 1968.

—— *Dragons in Amber*. New York, Viking, 1951.

—— *The Lungfish and the Unicorn*. New York, Modern Age, 1941.

Lucas, Frederic A. *Animals of the Past*. New York, American Museum of Natural History, 1929.

Lull, Richard Swann. *Fossils*. New York, The University Society, 1935.

MacGowan, Kenneth, and Hester, Joseph A., Jr. *Early Man in the New World*. New York, Doubleday, 1962.

Martin, Edwin T. *Thomas Jefferson: Scientist*. New York, Henry Schuman, 1952.

Montagu, Ashley, and Peterson, C. Bernard. "The Earliest Account of the Association of Human Artifacts with Fossil Mammals in North America." *Proceedings of the American Philosophical Society*, Vol. 87, No. 5, May 5, 1944.

Newell, Norman D. "Crises in the History of Life." *Scientific American*, February, 1963.

Nordenskiöld, A. E. *The Voyage of the Vega*. London, Macmillan, 1881.

Sanderson, Ivan T. *The Dynasty of Abu*. New York, Knopf, 1962.

Scheele, William E. *The First Mammals*. Cleveland, World Publishing, 1955.

Silverberg, Robert. *The Auk, the Dodo, and the Oryx: Vanished and Vanishing Creatures*. New York, Thomas Y. Crowell, 1967.

—— *The Challenge of Climate: Man and His Environment*. New York, Meredith, 1969.

—— *Forgotten by Time: A Book of Living Fossils*. New York, Thomas Y. Crowell, 1966.

—— *Man Before Adam*. Philadelphia, Macrae Smith, 1964.

—— *Men Against Time: Salvage Archaeology in the United States*. New York, Macmillan, 1967.

—— *The Morning of Mankind: Prehistoric Man in Europe*. Greenwich, Conn., New York Graphic Society, 1967.

—— *The Mound Builders of Ancient America.* Greenwich, Conn., New York Graphic Society, 1968.

—— *Scientists and Scoundrels: A Book of Hoaxes.* New York, Thomas Y. Crowell, 1965.

Simpson, George Gaylord. "The Beginnings of Vertebrate Paleontology in North America." *Proceedings of the American Philosophical Society,* Vol. 86, No. 1, September 25, 1942.

Walker, Ernest P. *Mammals of the World.* Baltimore, Johns Hopkins Press, 1964.

Wendt, Herbert. *Before the Deluge.* New York, Doubleday, 1968.

—— *In Search of Adam.* Boston, Houghton Mifflin, 1956.

Wormington, H. M. *Ancient Man in North America.* Denver, Denver Museum of Natural History, 1957.

Abbeville (France), 102, 103

Academy of Sciences, St. Petersburg, 51, 141, 147, 148

Adams, Mikhail Ivanovich, 50, 51, 53, 71, 81, 95

Adams Mammoth, 136, 139, 148, 150, 154

Agassiz, Louis, 109

Altamira, 125, 126

American Philosophical Society, 78, 84, 85, 87, 131, 213

Andrews, Charles W., 161

antediluvian, 14, 38, 79, 98, 102

Arabs, 28, 41

Archidiskodon, 165, 168, 171, 175

Archidiskon imperator, 153, 165, 168, 205

Aurignacians (*see* Cro-Magnon men) 117, 124

Avril, Father, 29, 32

Bartram, John, 57, 58

Beresovka mammoth, 141, 146, 147, 150, 179

Bering Strait, 189, 190, 200

Big Bone Lick, 57–59, 62, 64, 65, 67, 68, 70, 75, 76, 82, 85, 90, 91, 174

Bilgery, Father Conrad, 204, 205

Blackwater Draw, 205–207, 209

Blumenbach, Johann Friedrich, 46, 47, 51, 52, 63, 71, 81, 152

blood, 147

Boltunov, Koman, 49–51

Book of Job, 41, 42

British Museum, 131, 132

Buffon, Count de, 72–75, 77

carbon–14 dating, 149, 204, 205, 207, 208, 210–212

Cave paintings, 125–128

Chappe d'Auteroche, Abbé, 68, 70

Christy, Henry, 104–106, 125

Clark, William, 90, 91, 186, 187

climactic shift, 106, 108, 178, 214

Clovis people, 208–212

Clovis points, 206–208, 210, 213

Collinson, Peter, 64–68

Conradi, Horace P., 139, 140

Conyers, 23, 99

Cortés, Hernando, 17, 19, 56

Cotter, John L., 205, 206

Croghan, George, 59, 60, 62, 63, 68

Cro-Magnon men, 117–119

Cuvier, Georges, 79–82, 94–96, 98–102, 104

Daubenton, Jean Louis, 63, 64, 66, 70, 73

De Castillo, Bernal Díaz, 17, 19

deluge, 9–14, 16, 23, 34, 35, 55, 65, 79, 98, 99, 108

Dent (Colorado), 204, 205, 207, 208

De Perthes, Boucher (Jacques Boucher de Crèvecoeur de Perthes) 102–104

De Sautuola, Don Marcelino (*see* Marcelino, Don), 125

Díaz, Bernal (*see* Bernal Diaz de Castillo), 17, 19

Dickeson, Montroville Wilson, 197, 198, 201

Domebo (Oklahoma), 207–209
Dordogne, 105, 125
Dudley, Joseph, 16, 17

elephants, 19–24, 38, 46, 48, 59–66, 68, 70–77, 80, 95, 110, 111, 165, 175
Elephas primigenius, 48, 53, 71, 72, 81, 104, 152, 153
evolution, 157, 178, 182, 215
extinction, 65–67, 79, 175, 177, 178, 182, 215

Fayum Desert (Egypt), 161, 162
Figgins, J. D., 201, 202
Folsom points, 204, 205, 210
Franklin, Benjamin, 60–62, 67, 68, 85, 131

Gasconade County mastodon, 193–195, 211
giants, 9–16, 19
"giants' bones," 20, 21, 46, 53, 119, 214
glaciers, 108, 111, 190
Goforth, Dr. William, 90, 91
Gravettians, 117, 120, 124

Hakluyt, Richard, 29
Hannibal, 22, 23
Herz, Dr. Otto, 141–145, 148
hippopotamus, 42, 64, 66, 70, 73, 74
Howorth, Sir Henry, 175, 176
Hrdlicka, Ales, 200–202

ice ages, 108–111, 214
Ides, Evert Ysbrant, 32, 40

Jardin du Roi (France), 57, 63, 72

Jefferson, Thomas, 69–78, 83, 85–93, 174, 190, 214

K'ang-hsi, Emperor, 27, 32, 35
kill site, 204, 206–208, 211
King Louis XI, 11, 21
Koch, Albert, 129–132, 193–198, 201, 211

La Madeleine (France), 105, 106
Lange, Lorenz, 35, 36
Laptev, Khariton, 43
Lartet, Edouard, 104–106, 108, 125
Lehner, 206, 209
Leibnitz, Gottfried Wilhelm, 16
Les Combarelles (France), 126, 155
Lewis, Meriwether, 90, 91, 186, 187
Linnaeus, Carolus, 80
Logan, Josias, 29
Longueuil, Baron de, 56, 57, 63, 64, 92
Lyell, Charles, 101, 198

mammoth, 32–39, 41–46, 49–51, 62, 63, 69–75, 77, 81, 89, 91, 94, 98, 103–106, 110, 113, 116, 118–121, 124, 126–129, 135–140, 144–149, 151–158, 160, 161, 165, 175, 176, 183
Mammuthus primigenius, 153, 170, 178
man, 103–106, 111, 112, 189
Marcelino, Don (see de Sautuola, Don Marcelino), 125, 126
Masten, John, 84–86, 88

mastodon, 81, 82, 94, 128–130, 133–136, 163, 171, 174–176, 192

Mastodon americanus, 82, 130, 133, 174

Mather, Cotton, 16, 17, 19

Mazurier, 11, 12

Messerschmidt, Daniel Gottlieb, 42, 43

Missourium, 129–132, 194–196

Moeritherium, 161, 162

Mound Builders, 190–193, 197–200

Müller, Johan Bernahard, 37–39

Neanderthal man, 112, 113, 116, 118, 189

Noah, 9, 98, 101

Noah's Ark, 9, 13, 65, 68, 98

Osborn, Henry Fairfield, 171

Owen, Richard, 132

Paleoloxodon antiquus, 169, 170, 175

Paleomastodon, 162, 163

Pallas, Peter Simon, 95

Parelephas, 168, 169, 175

Parelephas trogontherii, 168, 170, 178

Peale, Charles Willson, 84–90, 129, 135

Peale, Rembrandt, 87, 88, 136

Peiresc, Nicolas, 19, 20

Peter the Great, 32, 35–37, 42

permafrost, 26

Pfizenmayer, E. W., 141–144, 146, 148

Philosophical *Transactions* of the Royal Society of London, 17

Powell, Maj. John Wesley, 199, 200

Predmost (Czechoslovakia), 118–121, 124, 128

prehistoric art, 104, 106, 125

prehistoric tools, 102–106

Presbuterian, The, 193–194

Puebla (Mexico), 213, 214

Riolan, Jean, 12, 19

rock shelters, 105, 106

Rome, 12, 22

Royal Society (England), 64, 65, 67

Royall, Mrs. Anne, 88, 89

Sevastianov, D. P., 141–144

Shelburne, Lord, 60, 64

Shumakhov, Ossip, 48–51, 95, 104, 140

Siberia, 24–26, 28, 29, 32–46, 48–50, 53, 61, 62, 70, 71, 142, 143, 183, 184

Sredne Kolymsk (Siberia), 143, 144

Steenstrup, Japetus, 118–121

taiga, 158, 160, 183, 184

Tarabykin, Semen, 140, 141

teeth, 56, 57, 60–65, 67–75, 78, 81, 84, 91, 99, 100, 160, 163–165

Tlaxcala (Mexico), 17, 19

Townsend, C. H., 138, 139

trunk, 162, 163

tundra, 26, 110, 113, 137, 142, 157, 158, 160, 183

Tunis, 19, 20

Turner, George, 78, 84

tusks, 16, 26–29, 31, 32, 34, 35, 38, 44–46, 51, 53, 58–60, 64–68, 70, 71, 73, 84, 91, 131, 156, 157, 160

Underground rat of the North, 27

Valence (France), 10, 11
vis plastica, 13, 14
von Strahlenberg, Baron Philipp Johann Tabbert, 39–42

war-elephants, 21–24
Warren, Dr., 134–135

weapon point, 201–202, 204, 205
Wistar, Caspar, 84, 92
Witzen, Cornelius, 34
Wolochowicz, Michael, 42–43
Wormbwell's Menagerie, 20, 21

Yakutsk (Siberia), 44, 45, 50, 51, 141, 147
Yavlovski, 140, 141
yen-shü, 27

ABOUT THE AUTHOR

Robert Silverberg is one of the most prolific writers of children's books today. He has several dozen books in print, both fiction and non-fiction, and has written many magazine articles. His books have won a number of awards, including: "New York Times Best Juveniles of the Year," "Herald Tribune Honor Book," and National Association of Independent Schools "Best Books." Mr. Silverberg was born and educated in New York and has been a professional writer since graduation from Columbia University in 1956.